Medical Receptionists and Secretaries Handbook

Second edition

Mari Robbins

Foreword by
Sir Michael Drury

Radcliffe Medical Press

© 1998 Mari Robbins

Radcliffe Medical Press Ltd
18 Marcham Road, Abingdon, Oxon OX14 1AA, UK

First edition 1996

British Library Cataloguing in Publication Data

A Catalogue record for this book is available from the British Library.

ISBN 1 85775 249 X

Library of Congress Cataloging-in-Publication Data

Typeset by AMA Graphics Ltd., Preston, Lancs
Printed and bound by TJ International Ltd., Padstow, Cornwall

Contents

Preface

The success of the first edition of this book published in 1996 has been responsible for the opportunity to produce a second edition of the *Medical Receptionists and Secretaries Handbook*.

This edition is published at a time of great change in the National Health Service which is now embarking on another journey of reforms, and managers, with the support of their receptionists and secretaries, are faced with the task of implementing the White Papers on both sides of the border.

The second edition has enabled me not only to incorporate changes which have taken place since 1996, but also to include new sections on issues reflecting the rapid changes taking place within the health service and to consider future changes that will involve all members of the health care team. The chapter on private medicine has been expanded to emphasize the role of the increasing number of receptionists working in this sector.

Times of change are never easy and professionals, their health care teams and patients tend to mistrust changes in their services. It is therefore important that all those involved in the provision of health care should have an understanding of what the changes involve and work as a team to ensure that the new National Health Service will lead to improved and effective health and social care based on identified patient needs. More than ever the medical receptionist and secretary will provide the vital link between patient and providers of health care within the national health and private sectors.

Mari Robbins
March 1998

List of contributors

Lynne Perry
Olive Tree
1 Minster Close
The Spires
Barry
CF63 1FL

Sally Storey
Director of Human Resources
Bournewood Community and Mental Health NHS Trust
Guildford Road
Chertsey
KT16 0QA

Foreword

One of the more significant features of health care development over the past three decades has been the gradual understanding of the central role of support services. Changes in the nature and provision of clinical care, changes in demography, and the increasingly complex character of treatment with greater numbers of skilled individuals involved with each case all pose problems.

Key figures in the support services are the receptionists and secretaries upon whom patients and health workers depend. To help with their development thirty years ago I wrote *The Medical Secretaries Handbook* and succeeding editions of that book marked the evolution in their roles and status as well as the changing systems within which they worked. This new book moves the process on further. It is written now by practitioners and teachers of the two occupations addressed and that itself says much about how matters have changed. Much that is contained within it really needs a wider audience and many other health care workers would benefit greatly from reading the sections on law and ethics, on audit and quality control and on information technology.

This Foreword does not do justice to the hard work and many wise things that Mari Robbins and her contributors have put into the book. It provides essential background reading that will be of interest to new entrants and to those who have been doing the job already. It covers hospital practice, general practice and work in private practice and will, I believe, become a well-thumbed reference book in the workplace as well as the standard textbook for students and those just entering the field of work. For those who design and run the various training schemes it will become an essential course book.

Two elements that occupy the central portion of the book are those referring to communication skills and patient care and this illustrates that in the pursuit of efficiency the prime target, helping the patient make sense of complex systems, is never lost sight of. I have no doubt that other editions will be required as further changes occur but I am equally confident that each edition will continue to provide a better understanding of the real function of us all – personal care.

Sir Michael Drury
March 1998

Acknowledgements

My acknowledgements and thanks go to: Jackie Coleman, Practice Manager to Dr S Woolf, General Medical Practitioner, Croydon; Margaret Godfrey, Senior Receptionist, Churchill Clinic, London; Glenda Webster, Practice Manager/Medical Secretary to Dr Anthony Yates, Consultant Rheumatologist, London; and Ivan Chu, Health and Safety Adviser, Bournewood Community and Mental Health NHS Trust.

The National Health Service

History

Prior to the National Health Service Act of 1946, health care in the United Kingdom had developed in an *ad hoc* manner.

The medical profession had, since the latter part of the 19th century, gradually acquired social respectability, legal status and economic strength. The concept of public responsibility for the health of individuals can be traced back to 1834 when the Poor Law Amendment Act was passed which established that parish workhouses should provide sick wards where the able-bodied inhabitants could be treated when they became unwell. However, as the health of the community had been severely neglected, it became necessary for the workhouses to admit the sick paupers from the parish to their wards, who, hitherto, had been left to die as they were unable to obtain medical care themselves. By 1848 the demand for institutional care was such that the sick wards of the workhouses had become entirely devoted to sick paupers. The Public Health Act of that year acknowledged for the first time the State's responsibility for institutional care.

The quality of medical care available improved as scientists made important discoveries. Florence Nightingale, in her contribution both to nurse training and hospital planning, revolutionized the standards of institutional care. Largely due to the philanthropy of the well-to-do and the moral obligations of the charitable and religious bodies, the end of the 19th century heralded the opening of many voluntary and private hospitals. Voluntary hospitals were financed through subscriptions and donations, and attracted the services of skilled doctors, some of whom, acting on their social conscience, treated patients often without payment.

The beginning of the 20th century brought about the advent of insurance schemes which enabled individuals to protect themselves against sickness and injuries which might involve them in expensive medical care or affect their capacity to work.

However, despite the progress that was being made, the standard of medical and nursing care emerging throughout the country was inconsistent both in quality and availability.

At the end of the First World War, the first Ministry of Health was established, which together with various reforms provided the stimuli for a nationally organized health service. The Second World War brought about further reforms and the publishing of the Beveridge Report in 1942 with its recommendations that formed the basis for the post-war system of social welfare services, and the provision of a comprehensive system of health care. Sir William Beveridge recommended that the term 'comprehensive' meant that medical treatment should be available for every citizen, both in the home and in hospital, and provided by general practitioners, specialist physicians and surgeons, dentists, opticians, nurses and midwives. He also advocated the provision of surgical appliances and rehabilitation services.

Thus the National Health Service (NHS) became effective in 1948, with the aim of improving the health of the people, to provide health care through a system of public finance and public provision and, by eradicating disease, to reduce the demand for free health care services. The NHS took over all hospitals, convalescent homes and rehabilitation units, offering consultants contracts as full-time salaried employees. General medical practitioners providing family doctor services were encouraged to sign contracts to provide family practitioner services for patients in their area, and were permitted to remain self-employed but paid by the health service on a fee basis.

Medical services fell into three functional areas:

- those concerned with the sick person in the community
- those concerned with the sick person in an institution
- those concerned with preventive medical services.

They were identified with the following services:

- general practitioner services
- hospital services
- services provided by the local authority (excluding school health services).

The hospital service was administered by regional hospital boards, under which were absorbed all the public and voluntary hospitals in the country. The national planning of hospital requirements was established.

Teaching hospitals in England and Wales remained relatively independent with their boards of governors who were responsible directly to the

Secretary of State, but they were linked only to the regional hospital boards in that there was one teaching hospital in each region.

General practitioner services were organized through executive councils, who administered the family doctors' contracts, dental, pharmaceutical and ophthalmic services. The local health authorities administered the preventive services, ambulance services, etc.

The main advantage of the NHS was that it had brought together the services which had previously been under the control of independent organizations. However, administration of this tripartite arrangement was far from satisfactory and in an attempt to improve co-ordination of health care between hospital boards, local executive councils and the type of care provided by local authorities, the 1974 National Health Service Reorganization Act came into force.

Reorganizing the NHS

The 1974 reorganization brought about changes in the way the NHS was organized and structured:

- the formation of regional health authorities (RHAs)

- the formation of area health authorities (AHAs) with directly accountable districts

- community health care, which hitherto had been the responsibility of local authorities, moved to the NHS

- executive councils were abolished and replaced by family practitioner committees (FPCs) to administer family practitioner services (general medical, dental and ophthalmic services, and the pharmaceutical services provided by retail pharmacists).

The changes introduced to the NHS the concept of planning and improvement in personnel and manpower controls.

Two issues arising from this reorganization and which remain today were the creation of:

- community health councils

- health service commissioner.

Community health councils

Community health councils (CHCs) were created with the 1974 reorganization (generally one for each health district), to represent the interests of the people in their community. Their main function is to make constructive criticisms and recommendations to the health authorities on the provision of services in their district. They also advise patients on how they may make complaints about the services.

Health service commissioner

Another feature arising from the 1974 reorganization was the appointment of the health service commissioner to investigate complaints within the NHS, giving complainants direct access to the commissioner. The commissioner will not investigate a complaint unless he/she is satisfied that the health authority concerned has had reasonable opportunity to look into and to reply to the complaint. Initially, the commissioner could not investigate areas covering family practitioner matters, but since April 1996 the proposals for a new complaints procedure, outlined in *Acting on Complaints*, confirmed that the Government would legislate to extend the jurisdiction of the health service commissioner (Ombudsman) to all complaints by, or on behalf of, NHS patients. The legislation brings within the Ombudsman's power complaints about:

- NHS services provided by family health services practitioners, their staff or deputies or locums
- actions taken wholly or partly as the result of the exercise of clinical judgement.

The Ombudsman is completely independent of the NHS and the Government. As well as complaints about the NHS services, he can investigate complaints about how the complaints procedure is working.

The Ombudsman is not obliged to investigate every complaint and will not generally take on a case which has not first been through the NHS complaints procedure.

Regional health authorities (RHAs)

The main responsibilities of the 14 RHAs in England included:

- strategic planning of health services
- capital building programmes
- postgraduate medical, dental and nursing training
- allocation of funds to area health authorities
- appointment of consultants and senior registrars.

Area health authorities (AHAs)

Ninety AHAs were set up in England with boundaries in most cases identical with those of local authorities.

Area health authorities were responsible for planning and providing services. They determined policies for care provision and put them into effect with the resources allocated by the regions.

The 1982 reorganization

The aim of this restructuring was:

- simplification

- to strengthen local level management.

The restructuring was intended to deliver greater efficiency and account-ability of the service to Parliament, including the direct responsibility of the Family Practitioner Committees to the Secretary of State and greater responsibility to manage their own affairs (see Figure 1.1).

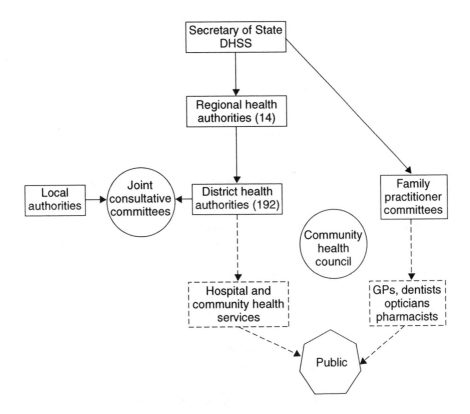

Figure 1.1   The NHS reorganization in England 1984.

Organization below district level

Below district level, health services were managed within units, and typically organized on the following basis:

- a large single hospital
- a group of smaller hospitals
- the community services of a district
- client care services, e.g. acute, mental illness or elderly.

Unit general managers were appointed to be responsible for all aspects of the services provided at unit level.

The changing NHS

The NHS in the early 1990s experienced a programme of reforms, more extensive and fundamental than any reorganization since its inception. The changes arose from proposals made in the three White Papers:

- Promoting Better Health – 1987
- Working for Patients – 1989
- Caring for People – 1989.

The Government stated that the proposal for reforms would not affect the basic principles of the NHS to provide:

> a comprehensive health service designed to secure improvement in the physical and mental health of the people of England and Wales, and the prevention, diagnosis and treatment of illness.

The reforms required certain statutory changes and these were embodied in the 1990 NHS and Community Care Act.

The most important of these reforms were:

- the introduction of a new system of contractual funding
- measures to manage clinical activity more effectively
- proposals to strengthen management at all levels
- new arrangements for allocating resources.

The NHS reforms and changes were intended to tackle the underlying problems in management and funding of the health service. By introducing competition between providers of health services in the form of an 'internal market', the Government intended to increase the efficiency and effectiveness with which resources are used. Services would also be more responsive to users by giving them greater choice. Providers of health services were encouraged to become NHS trusts, taking greater control over the management of their own affairs, including greater freedom to raise capital and to determine staffing structures and rates of pay. The 'purchasers' in this internal market would be either district health authorities (DHAs) or GP fundholders (GPFHs).

The organization of the National Health Service in the early 1990s

The basic structure of the NHS in England following the 1990 reforms is shown in Figure 1.2.

Figure 1.2   Structure of the NHS (Source: NHSE).

The Secretary of State for Health is responsible to Parliament for the provision of health services. The Secretary of State discharges responsibility through the various health authorities. Community health councils, as previously mentioned, are statutory bodies to represent the interests of their local community in the NHS.

As the NHS is almost entirely financed from public funds and with billions of pounds per annum voted to the NHS, Parliament expects some say in how that money is spent.

Department of Health

The responsibilities of the Department of Health cover three areas:

- health
- health care
- social services.

The NHS Management Executive (NHSME) was established in 1991 to have overall responsibility for the management of health services, whilst policy responsibility remained with the Department of Health.

Regional health authorities and NHSME outposts

RHAs were the intermediate tier between the Department of Health on the one hand and DHAs and family health service authorities (FHSAs) on the other. Sub-offices, known as 'outposts' of the NHSME were also set up to oversee the performance and development of NHS trusts.

District health authorities

Prior to April 1991 DHAs were responsible for managing local health services as well as planning and financing them. With the introduction of the reforms, they became responsible for assessing health needs of their local population, and purchasing hospital and community health services for them. There were 189 DHAs in England, each accountable to their responsible RHA.

Functions of district health authorities:

- Purchasing services for their local community, including services on behalf of non-fundholding general practitioners (GPs), and emergency services for all GPs, including fundholders.
- Managing directly managed units which remained under their control.
- Assessing the population's need for health care.
- Public health.

Family health services authorities

There were 90 FHSAs in England, serving populations ranging from 130 000 to 1 600 000. Each FHSA conformed to a major local authority area and generally followed the geographical boundaries of DHAs.

FHSAs managed the services provided by general medical practitioners (GMPs), general dental practitioners (GDPs), retail pharmacists and opticians. The terms under which family practitioners work are negotiated annually and FHSAs were responsible for implementing the practitioner contracts in their area. GMPs and GDPs are self-employed independent contractors to the NHS.

Functions of family health services authorities:

- Managing the contracts of family practitioners.

- Paying family practitioners in accordance with their contracts and for items of service provided.

- Reimbursement of allowances, etc. to practitioners.

- Planning and developing services to meet those needs.

- Ensuring that quality services were provided efficiently and cost-effectively.

- Carrying out consumer surveys.

- Monitoring medical audit in primary care.

- Monitoring indicative prescribing amounts.

FHSAs were also responsible for:

- approving surgery locations

- checking the standard of surgery premises

- hours of availability of family practitioners

- authorization and monitoring the use of deputizing services.

Special health authorities

Special health authorities administer some NHS services, responsible for specific areas of activity. They are accountable directly to the Secretary of State. Examples include:

- health authorities covering London's postgraduate teaching hospitals

- the Health Education Authority (HEA)

- the Mental Health Act Commission

- the NHS Training Authority (NHSTA).

Community health councils

Community health councils are statutory bodies established by RHAs and continue to represent the interest of the public in local health service provision and act as a channel for consumer concerns. Parliament has agreed that CHCs should have the following rights:

- to relevant information from local NHS authorities

- to access certain NHS premises

- to inclusion in consultation on substantial developments or variations in service

- to send observers to meetings of matching DHAs and FHSAs.

Purchaser/provider split

Since the 1991 reorganization of the NHS, the responsibilities for determining what health care is needed by the population and purchasing accordingly from a range of providers have been separated from those of providing hospital and community health services.

Purchasers

- *District health authorities* relinquished the job of running all hospitals and health units themselves, to buy the services needed by their local population from NHS trusts and other providers, including those in the independent sector.

- *Family health services authorities*, in close liaison with DHAs and local authorities, were also responsible for planning and developing services in primary care in order to meet local health needs.

- *GP fundholders* have their own budget to purchase some 'non-emergency' hospital treatments and community health services for their patients, for example; hip replacement surgery, hernia operations, cataract operations, etc. They can purchase from any provider of their choice. Budgets allocated to GP fundholders are subtracted from those of the DHA.

Providers

Most NHS hospitals and community units are now NHS trusts, providing services to DHAs and other purchasers on a contractual basis.

Services offered by private or independent sector health care providers may be purchased directly by patients through medical insurance, by DHAs or by GPFHs.

NHS trusts can be single hospitals and other health units (mental health services, community health services or services for people with learning difficulties), or a mix of hospitals and health units who have decided to work together, take responsibility for their own affairs and provide services. They were not responsible to RHAs or DHAs, but reported to the Department of Health through the NHS Executive.

Contracting in the NHS

Contracts provide the link between the purchaser and the provider. The contracts or service agreements (the Government has stated that such contracts are not legal documents) specify the costs, quality and quantity of care that should be provided.

The following summary will give secretaries and receptionists an understanding of the different types of contract they may come across in their day-to-day work.

Contracts for health care

Initially, contracts consisted almost entirely of simple block contracts. However, with the growth of GP fundholding and continuing changes in the health service and allocation of funding, we have seen a move towards more sophisticated contractual arrangements, which precisely define the services being purchased and which match payment more closely to the cost of service provision.

- *Simple block contract* – A fixed sum is paid for access to a defined range of services, although an indicative workload may be specified, over or under performance does not affect the financial payments. Block contracts were appropriate at the start of the internal market because of their administrative simplicity. Simple block contracts carry no financial risk for the purchaser, but resources may be wasted if anticipated workload fails to materialize. It is the provider who is at greater risk with a block contract as they may find themselves faced with more and more patients who cannot be turned away because of the urgency of their condition. Over performance against the contract may thus occur with no corresponding increase in funding.

- *Cost and volume contract* – Agreement is reached between the purchaser and provider prior to the financial year in which the activity takes place, whereby the purchaser pays a fixed sum for an identified volume of service. Beyond that level an additional payment is made for each episode of care usually at marginal or variable cost. A volume (financial) ceiling is usually agreed to limit the financial risk to which the purchaser is exposed. The provider's risk is reduced by being paid for what is delivered, although it can be difficult to balance many similar contracts.

- *Sophisticated block contract* – This type of block contract has emerged as a practical response to the reality of the internal market in which purchasers have cash-limited budgets which are usually insufficient to meet all potential demand. It is a hybrid of simple block and cost and volume contracts in which an agreed sum is paid for access to a defined range of services or facilities. Indicative volumes for work-loads are included, generally specifying the casemix, e.g. by specialty in a contract for acute services.

- *Cost per case contract* – As the name suggests, the purchaser pays a predetermined price for particular treatments as and when they arise. This type of contract may be used where very few patients are antici-pated to attend – for example, a specialist hospital. Cost per case con-tracts may expose health authorities to potential financial risk and to offset this a call-off contract may be preferred, specifying the upper financial limit against which individual cases can be charged. Cost per case contracts may be risky for the provider because fixed costs may not be covered if the anticipated workload fails to materialize.

- *Extracontractual referral (ECR)* – The provider requests authorization to treat a patient from outside the district of residence on an individ-ual basis. Each patient is regarded as an individual contract and the health authority/health board or GP fundholder will be invoiced accordingly.

- *Tertiary referrals* – Where a consultant has referred a patient to another consultant. The correct procedure must be followed to ensure payment (PPU1 Form).

Combinations or variations of the above contracts may be used to form any other type of contract.

The Health of the Nation

The Health of the Nation, published in 1992, was an outline of the intended national health strategy which focused on health outcomes as well as health care. The approach adopted was:

- select areas for action – or 'key' areas

- set national objectives and targets in key areas

- indicate the action needed by the NHS and other agencies such as local authorities to achieve the targets

- outline initiatives to help implement the action

- set the framework for measuring, monitoring, development and review.

The Health of the Nation initiative initially selected five 'key areas' with nationally determined targets, for example:

- *Coronary heart disease and stroke* – To reduce death rates from both coronary heart disease and stroke to people under 65 by at least 25% by the year 2000.

- *Cancer* – To reduce the death rate for breast cancer in the population invited for screening by at least 25% by the year 2000.

- *Mental illness* – To reduce the overall suicide rate by at least 15% by the year 2000.

- *Sexual health* – To reduce the incidence of gonorrhoea among men and women aged 15–64 by at least 20% by 1995, and to reduce the rate of conception amongst the under 16 year olds by at least 50% by the year 2000.

- *Accidents* – To reduce the death rate for accidents among children aged under 14 by at least 33% by the year 2055.

Health authorities were encouraged to collaborate and build alliances with local organizations (local authorities, voluntary sector, employers) to achieve the nationally set targets.

The Patient's Charter

Published in 1992, the Patient's Charter was the NHS version of the Government's 'Citizen's Charter' initiative. It emphasized patient choice and quality of care by setting out national rights and standards. Health authorities were encouraged to add their own local standards, and were held to account by the Department of Health for the publication of local charters and performance against certain standards. The most important of these included:

- maximum waiting times for inpatient treatment and outpatient appointment

- waiting times for assessment and treatment in accident and emergency departments

- numbers of cancelled appointments

- ambulance response times.

The range of standards was extended from time to time to encompass family doctor services, dental, optical and pharmaceutical services and community care. The Government started to publish 'league tables' of performance in 1995.

In January 1995, an expanded and updated Charter was published responding to views expressed by patients and introducing new standards in more areas and waiting time guarantees. A national standard for waiting for a first appointment as an outpatient was created.

In January 1997, the Department of Health published a booklet about NHS mental health services, explaining how the rights and standards in the Patient's Charter applies to people using mental health services. A separate booklet is also available applying to child and adolescent mental health services.

Community care

Following the 1990 Act, responsibility for securing care in the community passed to social services departments, together with certain changes in social security payments. This initiative, combined with the Government policy to end long-term institutional NHS provision for people with mental health problems or with learning disabilities, has led to the development of 'joint commissioning' arrangements, whereby health authorities and social services departments work together to secure community care for people in these groups.

Discrepancies in the provision of continuing health care for people with ongoing needs has led to the Government requirement for 'eligibility criteria' to be published by health authorities. They became effective from April 1996.

Quality of services

An important NHS goal is to improve the quality of services to individual patients, their carers and the wider community. In your own organization you may be part of a team involved in customer-care training, or developing an improved patient complaints procedure.

Audit

Clinical audit is the systematic and critical analysis of the quality of clinical care, including the procedures used for diagnosis, treatment and care, the associated resources, and the resulting outcome and quality of life for the patient (Policy Statement on the Development of Clinical Audit).

Clinical audit embraces the audit activity of all health care professionals, including doctors, nurses and other health care staff. Audit should:

- be professionally led
- be seen as part of an educational process
- form part of routine clinical care
- be based on setting standards
- yield results to help improve outcome of the quality of care
- involve management in the process and outcomes of audit
- be confidential at the individual patient or clinical level
- take into consideration views of the patient and carer
- be an important part of quality programmes.

Secretaries, receptionists and audit

Secretaries and receptionists play an important part in the process of patient care, through their administrative work and their contact with patients. They are often asked to participate in audit activity, for example:

- by recording the times patients arrive at the surgery or clinic, and the actual time they are seen by a doctor
- by attendance at an audit meeting to discuss ways of improving standards.

Remember, the patient's viewpoint and opinion plays an important part in audit, and both secretaries and receptionists are in a good position to hear this view expressed.

Further change: 'managing the new NHS'

Following a review of the 'functions and manpower', in late 1993 the Government published further proposals for change in the organization of the NHS, *Managing the New NHS*. The main thrust of these proposals was threefold:

The 'centre'

Structures were to be simplified and staffing numbers to be reduced in the Department of Health. The renamed 'NHS Executive' (NHSE) would be characterized by more strategic management to ensure accountability, while devolving responsibility to purchasers and providers at a local level. Functions of the NHSE would be:

- strategic framework
- policy development for health services
- research and development
- communications
- resource allocation to health authorities
- pay and human resource policy
- performance management and accountability
- public health.

Regional offices of NHSE came into being on 1 April 1994 to eventually replace both regional health authorities and NHSME Outposts.

Regional health authorities

Legislation was introduced in 1994 to allow the merger of the 14 'old' regions into eight new RHAs:

- North East and Yorkshire
- Trent
- East Anglia and Oxford
- North Thames
- South Thames
- South and West (incorporating the former Wessex)
- West Midlands
- North West (incorporating the former Mersey).

The eight RHAs were abolished from April 1996. Their functions have been partly devolved to new health authorities and partly taken on by much smaller regional offices staffed by civil servants.

'New' health authorities

During the early 1990s, many DHAs and FHSAs had begun to work closely together to act as health commissioning agencies across primary care and hospital and community health services. One of the main aims was to allow more flexible use of resources in response to trends in medical technology enabling services traditionally provided in hospitals to take place in GP surgeries and public preference for more locally accessible care.

The Health Authorities Act (1995) enabled DHAs and FHSAs to merge formally and this took effect across the country from April 1996, when they were known as 'health commissioning or health agencies'.

GP fundholding expansion

Ministers decided that early experiments in GP fundholding had been successful in improving the quality and efficiency of health care and enhancing patient choice. Therefore, the numbers of GP fundholders would be increased to cover 50% of the population by 1996 and the scope of fundholding would be expanded into three types:

- 'standard' fundholding, covering a wide range of elective procedures in hospital and community services, for practices with a patient list of over 7000

- 'community' fundholding, restricted to the purchase by GPs of community health services only, but enabling much smaller practices to participate in the scheme

- 'total fundholding', whereby practices or groups of practices would take over from the health authority the total budget for all hospital and community health services, including emergency services.

Role of new health authorities

The Government also set out the role expected of new health authorities:

- *strategy* – developing and implementing strategies for improving the health of the local population, having involved general practitioners in the process

- *monitoring* – checking the performance and accountability of GP fundholders in securing health services for their patients

- *support* – providing administrative support and management development to GP fundholders.

A primary care-led NHS

An 'executive letter', *Towards a Primary Care-Led NHS*, issued by the NHSE late in 1994 set out the next phase of the evolution of the Government's health reforms.

What is meant by a primary care-led NHS

In 1995 the Secretary of State for Health explained:

> 'In a primary care-led NHS two things need to continue: the primary care sector must continue to develop, and the secondary, specialist services must continue to respond to the needs of primary care and to work in closer partnership with primary care.'

The concept of a primary care-led NHS included the following principles:

- a recognition that 80–90% of NHS contact occurs in primary care
- an aim to provide the maximum range of services in the community close to where people live
- that services provided outside the patient's home and immediate community should be planned and delivered in a way that is patient-centred
- a closer partnership between primary and secondary care
- the close involvement of primary care professions in the planning and monitoring (commissioning) of all the area's health and social care
- an end to provider dominance without creating a GP dominated service
- the involvement of the public in decision making where possible
- the need to develop primary care in terms of adequate buildings, information and management infrastructure.

The imminent changes to the health service reflect many of the principles of a primary care-led NHS and recognized the need for a more responsive system based on integration and partnership.

The New NHS: modern, dependable

In December 1997, the recently elected Labour Government published its vision of a new NHS in the White Paper. *The New NHS: modern, dependable*.

The purpose of the White Paper is to provide patients with a modern and dependable NHS and it reflects the Government's commitment to restore and modernize the health service, abolishing the NHS internal market and replacing it with a new system of integrated care, based on partnership and driven by performance in a system which delivers better and more responsive health care into the next century.

The changes set out in the White Paper are guided by six key principles which aim to:

1   renew the NHS as a genuinely *national* service

2   make the delivery of health care against these new national standards a matter of *local* responsibility, based upon local needs

3   get the NHS to work in partnership

4   improve *efficiency* so that every pound in the NHS is spent to maximize the care for patients

5   shift the focus onto quality of care so that *excellence* is guaranteed to all patients

6   rebuild *public confidence* in the NHS.

The new system is designed to improve patient care by abolishing the internal market and bringing in mechanisms to improve and ensure high quality treatment and care where and when it is needed. It aims to harness the potential of new technology, and to improve effectiveness and efficiency through a new performance framework. The programme promises that patients will benefit from a better service every year.

A vision of an improved modernized NHS is:

- *at home* – access to advice and information about health, illness and the NHS

- *in the community* – speedy advice and treatment in local surgeries and health centres

- *in hospital* – prompt access to specialist services.

At home, everyone will be able to contact NHS Direct, a new 24-hour telephone advice line staffed by nurses. Three pilot care and advice helplines will begin in March 1998. By 2000, the whole country will be covered.

In the community, patients will benefit from faster test results, up-to-date specialist advice in the doctor's surgery and on-line booking of out-patients appointments by connecting every GP surgery and hospital to the NHSnet – the NHS's own information superhighway. There will be demonstration sites in 1998, and by 2002 these services should be available countrywide.

In hospital, everyone with suspected cancer will be able to see a specialist within two weeks of their GP deciding they need to be seen urgently and requesting an appointment. This will start for women with suspected breast cancer in 1999 and be extended to all other cases of suspected cancer by 2000.

Quality

The principle is that every part of the NHS and everyone who works in it should take responsibility for working to improve quality. This has to be quality in its broadest sense – doing the right things, at the right time, for the right people and doing them right first time. It must cover the quality of the patient's experience as well as the clinical outcomes – quality measured in terms of prompt access, good relationships and efficient administration. This will be achieved in three ways:

1 *National*

- a new evidence-based National Service Frameworks setting out national standards and guidelines to promote consistent access to high quality care across the country

- a National Institute for Clinical Excellence which will bring together work on clinical guidelines and cost-effectiveness.

2 *Local*

- local primary care groups will be formed to shape services for their patients

- explicit service standards in local service agreements between health authorities, primary care groups and NHS trusts reflecting national standards and targets

- a new system of clinical governance in NHS trusts and primary care.

A Commission for Health Improvement will be a statutory body set up to support and oversee quality, to tackle any shortcomings and to intervene where necessary.

3 *Efficiency*

The White Paper sets out six proposals to improve efficiency:

- clinical and financial responsibility will be united in new primary care groups which will be responsible for a single, unified budget covering most aspects of care

- management costs in health authorities and primary care groups will be capped

- the Department of Health will continue to bear down on NHS trust costs and bureaucracy. Extra-contractual referrals, cost per case and short-term contracts will be phased out

- there will be a national schedule of reference costs and NHS trusts will publish and benchmark their costs

- there will be clear incentives for all members of the local NHS to improve performance and efficiency

- there will be clear sanctions when performance and efficiency are not up to standard.

Structure

Figure 1.3 sets out the structure of the new NHS.

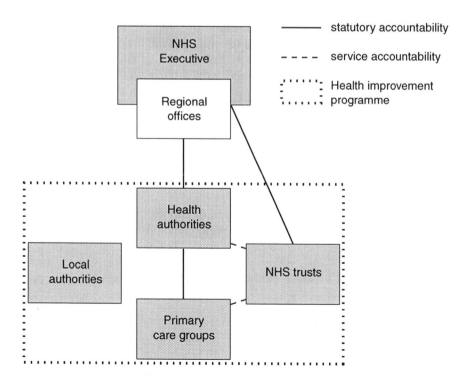

Figure 1.3   The new NHS.

The role of health authorities

Health authorities will play a lesser role as GP commissioning takes hold but they will be responsible for ensuring that GPs use funds effectively and efficiently (GPs will be largely responsible for purchasing services), and they will play an important role in the development of health improvement programmes.

Health authorities will be the accountable bodies under which primary care groups operate and they will hold considerable powers to improve the health of their local residents.

New commissioning groups

The Government proposes four commissioning models to eventually replace fundholding. This area of the White Paper is covered fully in Chapter 12.

Fundholding

The Government proposes to phase out fundholding (eighth wave fundholding has been officially deferred) and abolish the internal market, retaining the benefits of the system but removing the two-tier system which has led to unequal care for patients. It is proposed to replace GP fundholding with commissioning groups. Family doctors will have a choice of four commissioning models. (This is covered in greater detail in Chapter 12).

Health improvement programmes

Health improvement programmes (HIPs) will be developed by health authorities, commissioning groups, trusts, universities, medical schools, social services and other agencies. These programmes will address specific health needs and will guide commissioning patterns and ensure that improving local health is at the heart of the commissioning process.

Health action zones

It is envisaged that health action zones (HAZs) will bring together all those involved in delivering the NHS to develop a local health strategy in

co-operation with community groups, the voluntary sector, local busi-
nesses and local MPs. It is expected that community health councils will
be consulted.

Bids for HAZ status have already been invited and represent the beginning of an era of change within the NHS. They are intended to find new
ways on the ground for health and social services to work and commission
services together.

In April 1998, the first 11 health action zones were named in response
to bids submitted by health authorities, where projects ranged from a
community-based diabetic service to a drive to encourage more Asian
women to have cervical cytology. The funding allocated will focus on particular local problems and enable improvements in local health care.
Health action zones are expected to develop ways of involving patients
and the public in making decisions about local problems.

Trusts

Trusts will continue to be responsible for day-to-day management but will
also participate in the planning of local health improvement programmes.
Trusts will have new statutory duties on quality and partnership, and
service agreements with primary care commissioning groups will have to
include clear quality assurance standards.

Trusts will also have to demonstrate involvement of their staff, e.g.
greater involvement of clinicians in management, including them in
decisions on resources and planning with commissioners, as well as being
more open with staff about plans and giving them opportunities to
contribute ideas for improvement.

The first wave of 22 newly merged trusts starting on 1 April 1998,
reflected the Government's health service reforms.

NHS Charter

A new *NHS Charter* will be developed in partnership with NHS users,
carers and staff. It will emphasize more fully the quality of care and treatment, and aim to improve information available to the public. It is
proposed to publish a draft Charter some time during 1998.

Patient survey

The Government proposes to introduce a new national survey to
be carried out annually which will provide systematic and comparable

information on what users and carers feel about the NHS and the care it offers. The survey will be carried out at health authority level with results published nationally and locally.

Money

- Fundholding management costs will be redistributed to primary care groups.

- Health authorities will have responsibility for a single 'management cost envelope'.

- Extra-contractual referrals will be abolished.

- The Department of Health will announce a new management costs target.

- The White Paper states that the Government will free up to £1 billion from bureaucracy to patient care.

The future

The White Paper introduces a rolling programme of change but retains the best of current practices. It outlines a 10 year programme of improvement, with some of the changes taking place in the near future.

- NHS Direct – 24-hour advice line by 2000; three pilots during 1998

- GPs networked by 2002 – demonstration sites in 1998 in every region

- cancer appointments with specialist within two weeks of diagnosis by 2000

- breast cancer appointments will be within two weeks by 1999.

Designed to Care: renewing the NHS in Scotland (Scottish White Paper)

Proposals for the NHS in Scotland indicate that there will be only two types of trust:

- acute hospital trusts

- primary care trust.

Primary care trusts will be responsible for all primary health care, including mental health services and community hospitals together with general practices in local co-operatives. The health care co-operatives will replace GP fundholding and joint funds will enhance service provision between primary and secondary care.

Health boards remain accountable to the Scottish Office's NHS Management Executive. Trusts will be accountable to health boards for the implementation of five year health improvement programmes and be required to produce individual trust health improvement plans and publish a range of specified clinical performance indicators. Annual public meetings held by trusts will in future be held in conjunction with their health board.

The Scottish Ambulance Service will become a special health authority which should minimize the current problem of negotiating individual contracts with 15 health boards. The three island health boards will continue to have responsibility for strategy and day-to-day management through their directly managed units.

Health boards will be given new responsibilities to implement and maintain strategies set out in health improvement programmes and given powers of approval over capital planning, property and senior medical appointments.

Where possible it is intended that there should be one hospital trust in each health board area.

There will be a 'single stream of funds', as in England, to replace existing hospital and community health services and GP prescribing budgets. This will take place from 1 April 1998.

Putting Patients First (Welsh White Paper)

The Welsh White Paper, launched by the Welsh health minister in January 1998, has the same thrust as its English counterpart by retaining the purchaser–provider split in secondary care and emphasizing collaboration between different health organizations.

The Government has focused on the quality of services, e.g. a quality framework will be drawn up to improve services, and it has promised that by the end of 1998, women with suspected breast cancer will be seen by a specialist within five days of GP referral, and receive hospital test results within a further five days.

General practitioners and other professionals in primary health care will expand their role in commissioning health services for patients, but no primary care groups will be established in Wales. However, local health groups will be created with the same boundaries as Wales' unitary authorities and these will be sub-groups of health authorities. The White Paper states that all five Welsh health authorities will be retained, and required to draw up five year health improvement programmes for their areas. They will also be given new powers to ensure that trusts and local health groups act within these programmes. The Welsh Assembly will be responsible for assessing the needs of local populations, distributing resources and monitoring performance and outcomes.

Our Healthier Nation

The Government set out its public health plans in the launch of the Green Paper, *Our Healthier Nation*, at the end of January 1998. The document proposes a new 'contract for health with the people of England' promising to unite the nation in a drive against poor health. The new strategy is designed to replace *The Health of the Nation* and in place of the 27 target areas of this initiative, four key targets are incorporated in three key aims.
    Three key aims:

- increase the length of our lives

- increase the years we spend living life to the full

- increase the opportunities for a healthier and longer life for the many as well as for the few.

    Four national targets:

- heart disease and stroke – to reduce by at least one-third the death rate from heart disease and stroke in people under 65 years by 2010

- accidents – to reduce by one-fifth the rate of occurrence of major accidents to children and adults by 2010

- cancer – to reduce by at least one-fifth the death rate from all cancers among people under 65 by 2010

- poor mental health – to reduce by one-sixth the death rate from suicide and undetermined injury by 2010.

It is envisaged that health authorities will have important leadership roles in the implementation of *Our Healthier Nation* and will lead local alliances to develop health improvement programmes.

Summary

The development of the NHS reforms

1988

January Margaret Thatcher announces Ministerial Review of the NHS.

July Department of Health created following the splitting up of the Department of Health and Social Security. Kenneth Clarke appointed as Secretary of State for Health.

1989

January *Working for Patients* published.

November *NHS and Community Care Bill* published.

1990

June *NHS and Community Care Bill* receives Royal Assent.

November William Waldegrave replaces Kenneth Clarke as Secretary of State for Health.

1991

April NHS reforms come into operation. The first wave of 57 NHS trusts and 306 GP fundholders is established in England.

October The *Patient's Charter* published.

1992

April The Conservative Party is re-elected. Virginia Bottomley replaces William Waldegrave as Secretary of State for Health. The second wave of 99 NHS trusts and 288 GP fundholders is established in England.

July A White Paper on *The Health of the Nation* is published.

October The report of the *Tomlinson Inquiry* is published.

1993

February The Government publishes its response to the *Tomlinson Inquiry, Making London Better.*
A review of functions and manpower in the NHS is announced.

April The third wave of 136 NHS trusts and over 600 GP fundholders is established in England.

July The functions and manpower review reports to ministers.

October The Government publishes its response to the functions and manpower review, *Managing the New NHS*. This includes the proposed abolition of regional health authorities, the merger of district health authorities and family health services authorities, and a streamlining of the NHS management executive.

1994

April The fourth wave of 140 NHS trusts and 800 GP fundholders is established in England. The NHS management executive is renamed the NHS Executive and establishes eight regional offices. The number of regional health authorities is reduced from 14 to 8.

June   NHS performances tables published for the first time.

July   Department of Health publishes three reports setting out plans to streamline the role of the Department and the NHS Executive.

October   *Developing NHS Purchasing and GP Fundholding* published.

November   *Health Authorities Bill* published.

December   *The Operation of the Internal Market: local freedoms, national responsibilities* published.

1995

January   An updated *Patient's Charter* published.

April   The fifth wave of 21 NHS trusts and 560 GP fundholders is established in England. An accountability framework for fundholders is introduced.

June   *Health Authorities Bill* receives Royal Assent.

July   Stephen Dorrell replaces Virginia Bottomley as Secretary of State for Health.

November   Plans to use private finance initiative to build new NHS hospital announced.

1996

April   Regional health authorities are abolished and their functions taken over by NHS Executive regional offices. District health authorities and family health services authorities replaced by unitary health authorities. The sixth wave of 1,200 GP fundholders is established in England. Around 50 total purchasing projects go live.

May   Efficiency scrutiny into burdens of paperwork published.

June   Consultation paper *Primary Care: the future* published.

October   A White Paper on primary care, *Choice and Opportunity*, published. Reports of NHS funding problems.

November   A White Paper on the future of the NHS, *The National Health Service. A Service with Ambitions*, published.
The NHS (Primary Care) Bill published.
Additional resources for the NHS announced.

December   A second White Paper on primary care, *Primary Care: delivering the future*, published.

1997

May   Labour is elected and Frank Dobson is appointed Secretary of State for Health.

December   White Paper, *The New NHS: modern, dependable* published.
White Paper on the future of the NHS in Scotland, *Designed to Care*, published.

1998

April   First wave HAZs established. First wave newly merged trusts announced.

Reproduced with permission from Ham C (1997) *Management and Competition in the New NHS* (2nd ed) Radcliffe Medical Press, Oxford.

2

Patient (customer) care

The medical receptionist and secretary

Medical secretaries and receptionists are important, and sometimes undervalued, members of the health care team. Usually they are the first point of contact the patient has with a medical practice or a hospital department, clinic or ward. The receptionist's attitude, empathy and efficiency is able to either enhance or damage its image. A good receptionist can facilitate the way in which a patient accesses the system of medical care and should do all that is possible to make the patient feel welcome, comfortable and to ease the patient's access to medical help and care.

The first impression the patient has of the surgery or hospital department is usually of the reception area and the reception staff. Remember, the receptionist is the 'shop window' and the way in which patients feel as they sit in the waiting area will depend entirely on how the receptionist has reacted and greeted them. It is the receptionist's role to allay patients' fears and worries and help them to feel 'comfortable' whilst they wait. A courteous, friendly manner, accompanied by a smile and an understanding of the situation can work wonders, even with the most difficult of patients. The secretary, too, often has to reassure anxious patients and their relatives, and should adopt a similar approach.

Everyone, whether patients, secretaries, receptionists, doctors or other members of the health care team has feelings. If you have personal problems it is difficult not to allow your emotions to affect the way in which you respond and interact with patients and colleagues. It is important to be aware of this and have the ability to overcome your feelings. Your attitude will influence the attitude of the person you are dealing with. Remember, patients have personal problems too, and are often anxious or frightened, so your empathy of how the patient is feeling will do a lot to improve your own attitude.

How do you welcome patients?

Do you welcome them all in the same way?

Why do you treat people differently?

Why are some patients difficult when attending a hospital or GP surgery?

What are patients' expectations?

Have you experienced feelings of fear?

How do you react when frightened or worried?

How would you like to be treated?

Putting patients first

What is customer care?

Customer care means:

- giving the right impression
- meeting customers' expectations
- exceeding customers' expectations
- listening to customers
- having customer-friendly systems
- being totally professional
- putting customers first
- being totally customer orientated
- having the right attitude
- treating others as you would wish to be treated
- maintaining consistently high standards of service.

Remember the NHS is a very large business organization and the customers are your business

Customer care is not:

- a quick fix
- the flavour of the month
- a campaign which runs for three months, then stops
- just something for the receptionists
- something which brings instant results
- something which starts *after* the patient has reported to the receptionist.

What does the customer expect of us?

Customers have a variety of expectations about:

- the product and service
- staff
- the organization – hospital or GP surgery.

These expectations will include:

- welcoming, pleasant, smiling receptionists
- a concern for their needs
- interest and recognition
- value for money
- adequate information
- good support services
- satisfaction of their needs
- quality service.

Every patient/customer matters and deserves the best you and your practice, hospital or clinic can offer.

Creating the right impression

Some dos and don'ts for creating the right impression

DO	DON'T
Greet the patient pleasantly	Be rude
Make eye contact	
Use names	Be distant, or call everyone 'dear' or 'love'
Give your full attention	Be bored
	Talk to colleagues when patients need attention
Show respect for the patient	Criticize other members of the health care team
Be helpful	Be unco-operative
Say, 'May I help you'	Say, 'Can I help you'
Be confident	
Be positive	
Be efficient	
Be caring	
SMILE	

What improvements can be made?

By you?

By other members of the team?

YOU NEVER GET A SECOND CHANCE TO MAKE
A FIRST IMPRESSION!

A number of factors help create the right impression, including:

- layout
- space

- signs

- noise

- clutter/rubbish

- staff appearance

- staff behaviour

- facial expression

- tone of voice

- posture.

How to discover the customer's needs

Try to pick up any clues from what is said by the caller, and listen to the 'hidden' message. Do not jump to conclusions about the customer's needs; they are not always clearly expressed.

Follow up and probe by asking questions. Use 'open' questions, starting with:

- How?

- Why?

- What?

- When?

However, do not interrogate the customer.

Actively listen to discover the customer's needs

- Do not make hasty judgements.

- Do not let personal feelings or prejudices prevent you from listening to what is being said.

- Do not interrupt even if you feel you can guess the end of the sentence or remark.

- Do not forget to show that you are listening.

- Do not be distracted.

Body language or non-verbal communication (NVC)

Body language is an important factor in customer care. Remember it may reflect what you are really thinking! Body language should reinforce the spoken word. When it is contradictory, the customer may well believe the body language and not what is being said.

Important aspects of body language are:

- *Facial expressions and head position* – The face is mobile and can show a huge range of expressions. The expression on your face when you welcome the customer will affect their impression of you. Your head position is also important. Tilting your head to one side indicates interest in the other person.

- *Posture* – The way you hold your body is important. Observe people in your place of work and you will be surprised at the information you can get from their posture. Posture gives an indication of the level of interest in the customer: leaning slightly towards the customer suggests interest and concern; leaning away with arms folded indicates lack of interest or even boredom; standing with hands on hips is an aggressive signal.

- *Proximity* – We all need our 'personal space' – people who get too close to us will often make us feel uncomfortable and threatened. You should be close enough to customers to show interest – approximately three to four feet away is usually the best distance.

- *Eye contact and gaze* – Looking someone in the eye is generally felt to be a positive signal. Look directly at the customer, albeit briefly, when making the initial welcome. Not looking at them may indicate an attitude of not caring. However, some people avoid eye contact for reasons of shyness or of cultural tradition. Your eyes probably give the most expressive signal of all. Watch the customer's eyes during a conversation and you will get feedback of whether they understand/agree with what you are saying. Meet their gaze for approximately two-thirds of the time.

- *Body contact* – In our society it is not correct to touch a complete stranger. Generally the only acceptable form of touching is the handshake when greeting or saying goodbye to a customer.

- *Gestures* – Our gestures give a lot of information, for example, a nod or a shrug. Negative gestures include finger or foot tapping (impatience or aggression) and yawning (boredom).

- *Tone of voice* – We all give a deal of information to people, not by what we are saying, but by the tone of our voice. You may use welcoming words, but if you sound disinterested or angry you may cause the patient distress. Always ensure that your tone is as friendly as the spoken word.

A good technique is to mirror the customer's body language. Customer care and the telephone will be dealt with in Chapter 3.

Complaints within the health service

In recent years there has been increasing public awareness about quality of service. People have higher expectations about the service they receive. It used to be that people only complained if the quality of goods that they bought was shoddy, but nowadays people are equally concerned about how they are treated when buying their goods.

This applies also to the health service. People expect to receive a high standard of care and service. If they do not get it they are becoming more vocal about complaining.

Complaints are taken very seriously in the health service today. In order to develop and maintain a high standard of service we need to know when things go wrong. We need to know what has happened so that it can be avoided, and that action is taken to prevent it from happening again.

Also, we need to respond to our customers, the patients. If they don't get the service they expect, they need to know that they can complain and that their complaint will be investigated. They need to know that their complaint will be taken seriously and that they will receive an explanation and apology, if appropriate.

Moreover, quality standards are written into the contracts between purchasers and provider units. Complaints as an indicator of quality are monitored scrupulously by the purchasers. If a provider unit's services fall continually below the required standard, it is possible that their contract may not be renewed, thus threatening that hospital's very existence. Also, GP fundholders are unlikely to refer patients to hospitals where there is a high level of complaints about which no action is taken.

A key element of the Patient's Charter is the right to have any complaints about NHS services investigated and to receive a full written reply. In 1993 the Wilson Committee looked into the existing complaints procedure and found that it had become slow, cumbersome and difficult to access. As a result of the Committee's report a set of principles were agreed which should underpin any effective complaints procedure:

- responsiveness

- quality enhancement

- cost effectiveness

- accessibility

- impartiality

- simplicity

- speed
- confidentiality
- accountability.

These principles provide the foundation for the NHS complaints procedures introduced in April 1996. The procedure aims to provide a fair, simple and open system which is easy to access and enables lessons on quality to be extracted and used to improve services for patients. The prime aim is to resolve complaints and satisfy the concerns of the complainant through early, local resolution.

Why do patients complain?

Patients complain about a wide variety of different things:

- waiting times for a first outpatient appointment or to see the doctor in the clinic or surgery
- time on the waiting list
- lack of information
- not being kept informed of treatments
- staff behaviour and attitudes
- food
- cancellation of appointment or admission to hospital
- doctor not visiting patient at home
- cleanliness and building debris
- missing medical records, X-rays and test results
- missing property.

The person nominated by the practice or NHS trust to be responsible for dealing with complaints should give information about the procedure to the person complaining. This will include, where appropriate:

- how the complaint will be dealt with
- the purpose of the procedure
- the anticipated timetable
- the rules of confidentiality
- the availability of help from the local community health council

- possible outcomes of the procedure so that the person complaining may have realistic expectations

- the availability of conciliation services through the health authority or health board

- how to pursue a complaint with the health authority if the person complaining is not satisfied with the practice-based investigation

- the time limits for making complaints:

  - within six months of the date of the incident that caused the problem

    or

  - within six months of the date of discovering the problem, provided that is within 12 months of the incident.

The Patient's Charter gives patients the right to have a full and prompt written reply from the Chief Executive to any written complaint against a trust or health authority. The NHS tries to do this within four weeks of receiving any complaint. Where there are good reasons why this cannot be achieved, patients must be kept informed of progress.

The complaints procedure

The aim of the new system is to try to resolve most complaints close to the cause of patients' complaints – a doctor, nurse, receptionist, secretary or practice manager. In many cases it should be possible to sort out the problem straight away. This procedure is part of the local resolution mechanism for settling complaints in the NHS; health authorities and health boards can also contribute to the local resolution process through the provision of conciliation services.

If patients feel they have a reason to complain, they can do so directly to the medical practice or NHS trust concerned. However, health authorities or health boards have complaints managers who may be contacted by patients if they prefer to talk to someone who is not directly involved in their health care.

Complaints procedures in general medical practice

The terms of service of all family health practitioners have been amended to reflect these procedures. All practitioners are required to:

- have a practice-based system for handling complaints which must comply with the national criteria

- co-operate with their health authority complaints procedures, including independent review, if a complaint proceeds beyond the practice-based system.

National criteria for the NHS complaints procedure:

- complaints should be acknowledged within two working days
- an explanation should be provided within ten working days
- practices must publicize their complaints procedure
- written information on how to make a complaint must be available and include details of how to complain to a health authority or health board
- practices must nominate one person responsible for administering the complaints procedure.

Health authority and health board procedure

Health authority procedures are known as Independent Review. In all health authorities a senior member of staff is responsible for managing complaints. He or she works closely with a convenor who will be a non-executive director of the health authority or a person specifically charged by the board of the trust/health authority to act in this role, and who has responsibility for looking at complaints and deciding whether to agree a request for an Independent Review. The convenor will have access to independent medical advice from a doctor nominated by the Local Medical Committee (LMC). Health authority action must be flexible and does not, as with previous service committee procedures, need to follow strict procedures. The role of the convenor is to:

- refer the complaint back to the practice if it appears that the practice-based procedure has not been exhausted
- arrange conciliation where it appears that it might be helpful. Health authorities have to ensure that conciliation services are available to both parties
- set up an independent review panel to investigate the complaint
- take no further action where it is clear that everything that could be done has been done
- advise the complainant of his or her right to approach the Ombudsman.

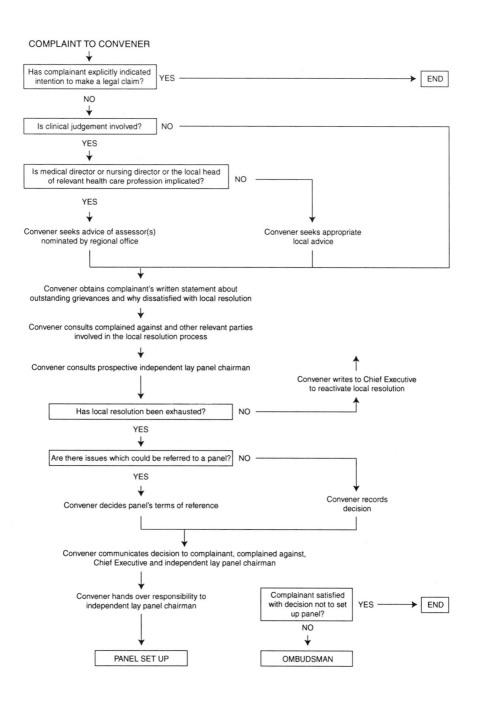

Figure 2.1   Convening a panel.

The Ombudsman

Most complaints should be resolved through one of the procedures. However, if a complainant remains dissatisfied, he or she is able to go to the Health Service Commissioner (Ombudsman). But further consideration is not an automatic right and the Ombudsman will decide on the merits of each case before embarking on a full investigation.

Receptionists and secretaries are advised to ask their managers for a copy of the complaints procedure used in their health care organization and for any points about which they are unsure to be explained.

Having a standard procedure also ensures clear communications. In fact, lack of communication is often the root cause of many complaints made in hospitals. A complaint about a relatively minor matter can become quite serious if it is not handled seriously in the first place. So, having a complaints procedure is better for patients and better for staff (see p. 35). It ensures that complaints are taken seriously, and that everyone involved has an opportunity to express their opinion. It encourages clear communication and by doing so may reduce complaints in the long term. It can help to improve the hospital's public image. More importantly, the major benefit of having a procedure is to ensure that the quality of service can be monitored, thus helping to maintain and develop high standards of care. A standardized procedure makes certain that the charter standard requirement for a full investigation and written response to all complaints from the Chief Executive is met.

How to meet the Wilson report requirements

- *Accessibility*: Promote the system with a patient information leaflet and poster, making it clear exactly who patients should approach.

- *Confidentiality*: Agree procedures, e.g. if a third party is involved, give no information without the patient's consent.

- *Impartiality*: Keep all complaints records and file them separately from the patient's medical records.

- *Responsiveness*: Keep patients informed at each stage about how long the complaint will take to resolve. Make them aware of the procedures they can follow if they are dissatisfied.

- *Simplicity*: Keep the procedure and patient information leaflets as simple as possible.

- *Speed*: Encourage complaints to be made quickly and handled as speedily as possible within the stated timescale. Delays can cause problems to escalate.

Taking customer complaints seriously

All complaints must be taken seriously. If a customer complains, it is an opportunity to put things right. All complaints should be:

- logged
- passed to the appropriate manager, and
- action taken.

Complaints should be dealt with immediately, and the customer should know the outcome as soon as possible. Remember, a complaint is any situation where the customer is not satisfied. If a complaint is handled well, the customer might feel more loyalty than before.

Dos and don'ts of complaints	
DO	DON'T
Get all the facts	Interrupt
Listen to what the customer has to say	Argue
	Justify
Apologize on behalf of the organization without making excuses	Make excuses
Show concern	
Tell the customer what will be done	

Patients expect:

- an apology, if appropriate
- a clear explanation
- assurance that action will be taken to prevent a recurrence.

Summary

Since 1996, the emphasis in complaints handling has been on local resolution with the underpinning principle that every effort should be made to satisfy the complainant's concerns as early as possible. Procedures have been rewritten to ensure that they are responsive, cost effective, speedy, promote accountability and respect confidentiality – adversarial encounters are to be avoided wherever possible. NHS trusts have 20 days to achieve a resolution and GP practices 10 days, and where a resolution has not been achieved, complainants may be offered an Independent Review Panel. Each health service organization designates a convenor, who examines the facts and decides whether a panel is to be convened. If so, the role of the panel is to decide on the balance of probabilities and whether to uphold the complaint.

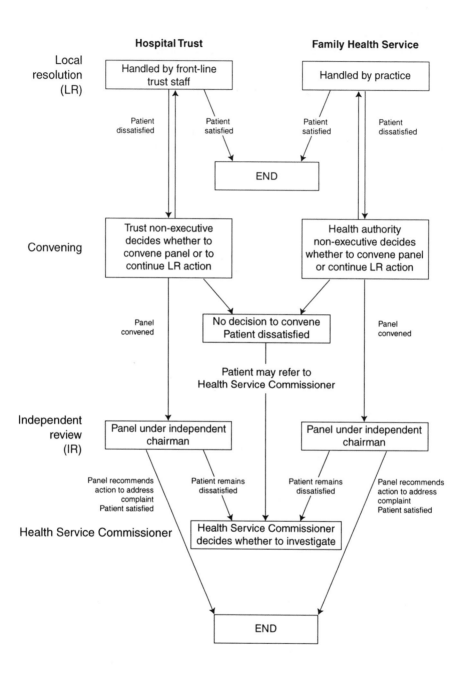

Figure 2.2   Complaints procedure.

Final impressions

The patient must go away feeling satisfied with the level of service you have given. They should feel that you:

- have been willing to help
- have taken a lot of trouble
- are more co-operative than others.

This will give a good impression of:

- you
- your skills as a secretary or receptionist
- your medical practice or your hospital.

Don't take customers (patients) for granted.

Summary

Customer care means that medical secretaries and receptionists should ensure:

- that your customers are, and feel, welcome, e.g. the way you greet them when they arrive will show them how you care
- that you show concern for the customer's needs, e.g. by the way you listen when they are asking a question or explaining something
- that you are interested, friendly and pleasant, e.g. being courteous at all times
- that you know what you are talking about, e.g. the services your hospital, practice or clinic offers
- that the services are the best
- that you recognize each customer as an individual person.

The medical secretary and receptionist and customer care

An experienced receptionist's or secretary's responsibility can be boundless and very fulfilling. They are able to assist and understand patients' medical conditions and help accordingly. They may arrange for a wheelchair, a porter or generally help. They will notice if a patient appears to be distressed and point it out to a nurse or doctor if they think it necessary. On a practical issue, they will keep the reception area generally tidy; magazines will be up to date and in good condition. Toys for children will not become a hazard to waiting patients but kept in a special play area. Plants and flowers will be fresh and watered when necessary. In a private hospital or practice, coffee will no doubt be offered to patients while they wait.

Developing your personal effectiveness

Being assertive

Being assertive means treating other people with respect, asking for what you want and not blaming others for what happens to you. It stems from taking an honest look at strengths and weaknesses and accepting them. Assertive behaviour can include some or many of these mannerisms:

VOICE	steady, firm tone is mid-range, rich and warm sincere, clear
SPEECH PATTERN	fluent emphasizes key words steady, even pace moderate speed
FACIAL EXPRESSION	responsive, matching the feelings expressed open steady features attentive interested
EYE CONTACT	direct maintained
BODY	relaxed open hand movements (inviting to speak) sits upright or relaxed (not cowering or slouching) stands with head held up

This type of behaviour makes other people feel good when they talk to you because you value them and accept their behaviour, and you are not crushed or threatened by rejection because you do not depend on others for approval.

Managing time

To be effective at work, good time management is essential. The boxes below identify some of the problems of poor management of time, the causes and some possible solutions.

PROBLEMS	CAUSES	POSSIBLE SOLUTIONS
Having too much to do	Unclear priorities	Check goals or tasks clearly with your manager and check priorities. Each day, decide on your priorities and stick to them
	Wanting to be directly involved with everything	Be selective, delegate if you can
	Unrealistic time estimates	Recognize that everything takes longer than you think – add 20% to your estimates
	Overwhelming pressure and piles of paper	Don't confuse activity with effectiveness – just because you are busy does not mean that you are working well. Try to get into a fixed daily routine with definite times for such jobs as sorting the post, filing, etc.
Inability to finish things	Lack of deadlines	Always set deadlines
	Lack of respect for your time and interruptions by others	Fix a regular time when you need to be left undisturbed. Arrange to divert 'phone calls, and agree to accept colleagues' calls in return. Be sure you know what you want to achieve so that you can communicate this to others
	Doing too many jobs at once	Do one job at a time. When you start a piece of work try to finish it if you can. You waste time each time you have to go back to it, while you remember where you had got to. Be systematic, because if you have to leave a job part finished, it will make it easier for you, or indeed anyone else, to pick it up again

Wasting time	Handle telephone calls promptly and write messages down immediately. When you make calls, plan what you are going to say beforehand and have all the necessary information to hand
Lack of overview and perspective	Know your priorities. Use your diary. Try to transfer responsibility for some of your work when taking on new jobs. Fix a specific time for any major jobs which should not be interrupted
Laziness	Impose deadlines on yourself and tell others about them

Looking after yourself

There is greater emphasis than ever before on health care staff to work to maintain and improve the health of the community they serve. A variety of initiatives come quickly to mind – antenatal and postnatal care, family planning, child development and immunization clinics, screening (well-man, well-woman, elderly), health promotion programmes for specific conditions (e.g. diabetes, hypertension, asthma), healthy eating and anti-smoking advice, health education literature and posters.

In a more general sense, everyone knows, in theory at least, that they should take certain basic sensible steps to maintain a healthy lifestyle, but for this to become a reality each individual has to understand how they can help themselves to avoid health problems. In doing this, they will also be contributing to their own personal effectiveness at work and at home.

Whether a doctor, receptionist, secretary, or nurse, the message is clear. You will do no one a good service if you do not build in time for looking after yourself.

Paying attention to our own health means taking a hard look at those factors known to contribute to poor health, including smoking, drinking to excess and being overweight, and making a conscious effort to take exercise, eat healthily and take advantage of all the health screening checks available.

Handling stress at work

Most people when discussing their jobs would refer somewhere to the amount of pressure they are under at work. Hopefully this will not be a constant problem, and in fact many people claim to work better when under slight pressure. The problems arise when the pressure becomes too great or continues for a long time.

An awareness of the difference between pressure and stress is important. Generally speaking, stress does not produce a positive or energetic response, but is reflected by panic reactions, irritability, an inability to relax and difficulty with relationships. It is also well known and well established that stress can lead to a variety of medical problems.

Stress at work may have a number of causes. The job may require a great deal of effort, rapid decision making, or its requirements may be ambiguous and therefore leading to competing demands. Unsatisfactory work conditions, inconsiderate bosses or supervisors, shift work and so on can all place pressure on an individual's ability to cope.

Stress is a fact of life and cannot be eliminated. Indeed most people would become quickly bored if too few demands were placed upon them. The key issue, therefore, is that of coping; that is the response made by an individual who encounters a situation with a potentially harmful outcome. Most people use an enormous number of ways of coping with diverse demands, and often different combinations of different types. In general terms there are two major functions of coping. One is to alter the situation causing stress, the other is to deal with the emotion that the stress engenders. The extent to which an individual is able to deal with these two aspects depends on a variety of circumstances. However, the fact that they both have an impact in varying degrees can help in understanding situations better and in developing coping strategies.

Flexibility is important. It is more effective to use a variety of coping skills than one specific response. It is necessary therefore to be cautious when taking on board any fixed ideas on how to cope. However, there are some general guidelines which can help one to think through the situation:

Know yourself and the way you react

Relax

Decide what is important

Look for support from others

Keep communicating

Use a step-by-step, problem solving approach

Patients' rights and National Charter standards

The Patient's Charter, introduced in April 1992, established ten patients' rights and nine specific National Charter standards, which form a central part of the Government's programme to improve and modernize the delivery of the service to the public.

The Patient's Charter

Generally speaking, the Patient's Charter aims to raise the standard of health care provided by the NHS by:

- putting patients' needs first

- providing services that produce evident benefits to people's health

- being an efficient system through better management

- respecting and valuing those who work with and for the NHS.

The National Charter standards are not legal rights as such, but specific standards which the Government looks to the NHS to achieve, as allowed by circumstances and resources.
   The standards are:

- *Respect for privacy, dignity and religious and cultural beliefs* – All health services should make provision so that proper personal consideration is shown to the patients, for example by ensuring that privacy, dignity and religious and cultural beliefs are respected. Practical arrangements should include meals to suit all dietary requirements, and private rooms for confidential discussions with relatives.

- *Arrangements to ensure that everyone, including people with special needs, can use services* – All health authorities should ensure the services that they arrange can be used by everyone, including children and people with special needs such as those with physical and mental disabilities; for example, by ensuring that buildings can be used by people in wheelchairs.

- *Information to relatives and friends* – Health authorities should ensure that there are arrangements to inform relatives and friends about the progress of a patient's treatment, according to their wishes.

- *Waiting time for an ambulance service* – When an emergency ambulance is called it should arrive within 14 minutes in an urban area, or 19 minutes in a rural area.

- *Waiting time in outpatient clinics* – A patient should be given a specific appointment time and be seen within 30 minutes of that time.

- *Cancellation of operations* – A patient's operation should not be cancelled on the day he or she is to arrive in hospital. It is acknowledged, however, that this can happen because of emergencies or staff sickness. If, in exceptional circumstances, an operation has to be postponed twice, the patient should be admitted to hospital within one month of the date of the cancelled operation.

- *A named, qualified nurse, midwife or health visitor responsible for each patient* – Each patient should have a named, qualified nurse, midwife or health visitor who will be responsible for their nursing care.

- *Discharge of patients from hospital* – Before a patient is discharged from hospital, a decision should have been made about any continuing health or social care needs that they may have. The hospital has to agree arrangements for meeting these needs with agencies such as community nursing services and local authority social services departments before the patient is discharged. The patient and his or her carers should be consulted and informed at all stages.

Local charter standards

In addition to the stated National Charter standards, the Government requires health authorities to set clear local standards on areas, including:

- waiting times for first outpatient appointments
- waiting times in accident and emergency departments, after the patient's need for treatment has been assessed
- waiting times for taking patients home after treatment where NHS transport is used
- enabling patients and visitors to find their way around hospitals, through enquiry points and better sign posting
- ensuring that staff who deal with patients face-to-face wear name badges.

An extension to the Patient's Charter announced the first national outpatients target:

- Nine out of ten patients referred to hospital by GPs or dentists can expect to be given an appointment within 13 weeks, and everyone can expect to be seen within 26 weeks.

At the same it was announced that:

- The guarantee of a maximum of 18 months' wait for hip, knee and cataract operations is to be extended to cover all admissions to hospital from April 1995.

- In addition, from April 1995, patients can expect treatment within one year for coronary artery bypass grafts and some associated procedures. (If the consultant considers the need for treatment is urgent, patients can expect to be seen more quickly.)

- From April 1995, patients admitted to hospital through an accident and emergency department can expect to be given a bed as soon as possible, and certainly within three to four hours. From April 1996 this standard has been improved to two hours.

Hospitals and trusts are expected to provide enquiry points and clear signposting in hospitals and patients can expect to be cared for in an environment which is clean and safe. Hospitals and trusts are expected to set local standards on:

- waiting times in accident and emergency departments after the need for treatment has been assessed

- waiting times for taking patients home after treatment if there is a medical need for NHS transport.

In addition, hospitals and trusts should:

- display information on the Patient's Charter including local standards and whether they are meeting them

- make it clear to patients how they can complain or make comments/suggestions whilst in hospital

- publish on a regular basis details of the numbers of complaints they have received and time taken to deal with them.

Note that expectations are standards of service which the NHS aims to achieve.

The Patient's Charter and the family doctor service

This was published in March 1993 by the Department of Health and the Central Office of Information, and was designed to raise the standards of general practice. However, it sets out the minimum requirements and states that every person in the country has the following rights:

- to be registered with a family doctor

- to change doctor quickly and easily

- to be offered a health check when joining a doctor's list for the first time, or at home yearly, if 75 years old or over

- to receive emergency care at any time through a family doctor

- to have appropriate drugs and medicine prescribed

- to be referred to an acceptable consultant when the family doctor thinks it is necessary, and to be referred for a second opinion if the patient and family think it desirable

- to have access to personal medical records, subject to any limitations by law

- to know that those working for the NHS are under a legal duty to keep the contents of health records confidential

- to choose whether or not to take part in medical research or student training

- to be given detailed information about local family doctor services through the local health authority (HA) directory

- to receive a copy of the doctor's practice leaflet, setting out the services he or she provides

- to receive a full and prompt reply to any complaint made about NHS services.

A new NHS Charter will be developed in partnership with NHS users and carers and a draft Charter is proposed for 1998.

Mental health services

A 1997 Department of Health publication clearly states how the rights and standards in the Patient's Charter apply to people using adult mental health services. It gives information about care under the Mental Health Act and explains how in some circumstances the Mental Health Act overrides a certain right, such as the one to choose whether to receive treatment.

Community care

Local authorities should have a charter covering community services for people with mental health problems who are receiving care in the community.

Access to health care

The first two National Charter standards particularly relate to access to health care for all:

1   respect of privacy, dignity and religious and cultural beliefs
2   arrangements to ensure that everyone, including people with special needs, can use the services.

Consider the ways in which medical secretaries and receptionists ensure that all patients receive the best service and support. This will mean attending to:

- the general needs of all patients and visitors

- the special needs of some patients, especially those of mobility, disability, elderly and ethnic minorities

- patient transport.

Many patients, some of whom will also have special needs, are anxious and uneasy about their visit to the surgery or hospital. The receptionist is usually the first person that a patient will communicate with, and the special skills, knowledge, understanding and empathy that the receptionist uses when receiving and dealing with them are most important.

Patients' general needs

Secretaries and receptionists should be able to answer all queries about the services offered by the practice or hospital department and to direct patients and give appropriate information, for example:

- waiting area

- clinic or surgery times

- relevant consulting room

- toilet, including disabled facilities

- changing facilities

- refreshment facilities (machines, snack bar, etc.).

Patients' special needs

'Disabled' means not being able to do some of the things that able-bodied people can do. A recent survey shows that approximately 15% of adults have some form of disability.

Disabilities may be present from birth, or be the results of accident or disease, which may require a change in lifestyle. However, an ever-increasing group of disabled people are those whose disability comes with age.

The main types of disability are:

- difficulties in mobility

- impaired sight or hearing

- learning difficulties.

People with mobility difficulties may include patients with multiple sclerosis, spina bifida or injury, who are unable to walk and confined to a wheelchair; or the elderly who walk slowly and awkwardly. People with learning difficulties also include those who have difficulty in reading or writing, which still commonly occurs.

Problems may arise when a person with a disability visits the surgery or hospital and may be due to:

- the premises

- the staff

- the patient.

Premises

Look at your place of work in a detached manner and imagine how it must be for a disabled person. Can a patient in a wheelchair readily gain access to the surgery premises or to your hospital department? Are there steps? Are the doors sufficiently wide for wheelchair access? Where can the wheelchair be placed in the waiting area? Is there good light at the reception desk to aid lip-reading? Is there an area or room away from the reception desk where confidential matters may be dealt with, or for a private discussion with a deaf person? Are the notices clearly written and easy to read?

Staff

Empathy is the most important quality for any staff dealing with patients, more so when dealing with disabled patients. Staff should be aware of the disability and anticipate what the difficulties may be, for example, sitting in a waiting room, worrying that a call may be missed makes a deaf person very anxious. Secretaries and receptionists should be tactful and relate to the patient, help with the difficulties caused by the disability and allow more time to deal with their special needs.

Patients

You will find that the majority of patients with a disability are usually less demanding than many other patients. They try to be as independent as possible, although very much aware that special allowances may have to be made because they may be slower, or require things to be written down for them, or, if in a wheelchair, take up more space in the waiting area.

Secretaries and receptionists should be aware that some patients will try to hide their disability, and you should respect their wishes by offering advice without drawing attention to their problems.

Elderly patients

The medical secretary or receptionist should be aware of the many and diverse problems which may affect an elderly patient's access to health care, and try to minimize the effect of some of the following problems which may be encountered:

- impaired hearing

- impaired eyesight

- decreased mobility

- difficulty or inability to cope with new procedures

- reduced energy

- arthritic joints

- fear of being misunderstood

- fear of not understanding instructions

- desire not to be a nuisance to doctors and staff

- socio-economic problems, e.g. financial problems, loneliness, increasing difficulty in day-to-day living.

Cultural issues and language barriers

Medical secretaries and receptionists should be able to identify an individual patient's ethnic or cultural needs and remember that their manner and the way in which they communicate with patients is important in ensuring that ethnic or cultural requirements are identified and met. Remember that, if a patient is discourteous to you, it may be that they have difficulty in expressing themselves or because they are worried about their medical condition. Remain professional, polite and calm at all times.

Interpreters

Good communication plays a vital role in the provision of effective health care. Many patients, especially in inner-city areas, may have a very limited knowledge of the English language and an interpreter may have to be used.

An interpreter may be available in some hospitals, or colleagues within the workforce may be able to help. On the other hand, interpreters are available from external sources and receptionists and secretaries should know how to contact them if it is felt that an interpreter may be of significant help to improve communication and understanding.

Patients may be accompanied by a relative or friend who is more fluent in the English language, when attending surgery or a hospital clinic, to facilitate communication.

Remember that there are still many people in this country who are illiterate. You should be particularly aware and sensitive when offering your help, as they are often extremely embarrassed.

Staff working in general practice will, no doubt, have a list of interpreting services available locally, or will be able to obtain information from their local authority social services department.

The decision as to which is used is dependent upon the purpose for which the interpreter's services are required.

External interpreters should be used:

- for formal communications, for example, interviews, complaints procedures, etc.

- if requested by the patient, relative or fellow professional involved in the care of the patient

- if professional services are deemed to be necessary to enhance understanding.

Visually impaired people

Guidelines are available from the Royal National Institute for the Blind (RNIB) for the provision of a 'user-friendly' environment for people with poor eyesight. These guidelines give suggestions for improving visibility and to providing tactile and auditory clues.

Visibility

Appropriate lighting is the most important aid to vision. People with visual impairment will need twice the quantity of light than sighted people. As people get older, the need for effective lighting increases. The *decor* of the surgery or hospital should reflect the needs of people with impaired sight and the use of contrasting colours will reduce disability. *Shiny surfaces* create reflection and glare; if possible, they should not be used. *Obstructions* must be kept to a minimum and highlighted. Be aware of potential hazards to the visually impaired:

- furniture
- planters
- toys left on the floor.

Ideally, all edges to furniture and walls should be rounded to minimize injury in the event of a collision. *Signs and notices* should be clearly written to be effective.

Any *auditory clues* that may be used must be direct, useful and readily understood.

Tactile clues and texture contrasts can be underfoot, or at a suitable height for hand/finger touch, enabling the visually impaired person to identify a particular area, etc.

All staff who have contact with visually impaired people can do much to facilitate their access to health care.

- Ensure that all instructions are clear and readily understood.
- If necessary take the person to a seat (they may not be able to see it); guide their hand to touch the seat or back of the chair.
- Take them to the doctor's consulting room, or to the nurse.
- Arrange help if they need to go from one hospital department to another.

- Help patients with poor eyesight to fill in forms; if they need to sign their name, place their finger on the place of signature.

- When addressing the patient, use their name, or touch them so they know you are talking to them and not someone else. When you leave them, don't forget to tell them, so that they do not continue a conversation with someone who is not there.

- Use speech appropriate to people with impaired sight.

- Make sure they are sitting safely, and so that the doctor or nurse can see them.

People with hearing difficulties

Patients who have hearing difficulties or who are totally deaf may like to communicate in writing, so make sure you have a supply of pens and paper for this. Perhaps members of staff may be able to use sign language.

If you are dealing with appointments, it is a good idea to make a note in the appointments book of any such patients, so that they are not overlooked when their name is called out and thus miss their appointment.

The following points will help you to communicate effectively with people who have hearing difficulties:

Face-to-face

- Speak up, but do not shout.

- Speak a little more slowly than usual.

- Maintain eye contact.

- Ensure your face is well lit.

- Make sure that the person can see your face clearly to help lip reading.

- Do not look away from the person when talking to them.

- Write it down if you cannot get the message across.

Telephone

- Speak up, but do not shout.

- Speak more slowly than usual.

- If you are not understood, do not repeatedly use the same words, but rephrase what you are saying.

- When giving letters, use letters of the alphabet to clarify ('A' apple, 'C' Charlie, etc.).

- When giving numbers, appointment dates, etc., always ask the person to repeat to ensure understanding.

People with learning difficulties

Staff working in both general practice or hospital will find they are dealing more and more with people with learning difficulties, who are now living in the community, and have the same access to health care as anyone else. It is important that they are treated in precisely the same way, but making allowance where necessary to ensure they get the best out of the health service. Therefore:

- be patient

- do not be intimidated – frustration at not being able to make themselves understood may make them appear aggressive

- stay calm

- ignore any strange mannerisms and comments

- speak in simple, straightforward language.

Remember, there are still patients who are illiterate and experience problems in accessing health care, perhaps when telephoning for an appointment for pathology or ante-natal clinic, for example. Although they may not be able to read what is written down, they may well be able to name individual letters, so be patient and ask them to give you the letters forming the written word, rather than the embarrassment of admitting to you that they are unable to read.

Children

Many children each day attend their doctor's surgery, the local hospital or community clinic. Everything should be done to provide for children's needs:

- a play area

- sturdy toys

- colourful books

- a changing area for babies and toddlers.

Again, if possible, chairs and tables in waiting areas should have rounded corners to prevent serious injury.

Children are often frightened by a surgery or hospital, so staff should be sensitive to the special needs of children and do all they can to provide a safe, reassuring and friendly environment.

In 1993 the Audit Commission published a report *Children First* on the care of sick children. The report examined six principles of care and gave guidance as to how each should be adopted:

- *Child and family-centred care* – Hospitals should be sensitive to the special needs of children and their families when in hospital, placing as much emphasis on the care and support of the child (which means the involvement of parents in their care) as on their medical needs. Services also need to be tailored to the wide range of children (from under one up to and including 18 years).

- *Specially skilled staff* – Children should only be cared for by staff specially trained to meet their particular needs.

- *Separate facilities* – Children should only be cared for in facilities which are designed with their needs in mind. Where separate designed facilities do not exist, children should not be treated in other parts of a hospital.

- *Effective treatments* – Children should only receive treatments which are known to be effective.

- *Appropriate hospitalization* – Children should only be admitted to hospital when the treatment and care cannot be provided in an alternative environment, e.g. their home.

- *Strategic commissioning* – Purchasers should be commissioning the types of service which most meets children's needs, particularly the development of hospital-at-home services to avoid hospitalization as far as possible.

- *The National Association for the Welfare of Children in Hospital (NAWCH)* has added to these in its Charter for Children in Hospital.

Working people

General practitioners and hospitals alike are becoming aware of the need to improve access to health care for working men and women by offering appointments at times better suited to their working hours. As a result surgeries and clinics are either offering appointments earlier in the morning, later in the evening, or reserving the first appointments for business people. Similar consideration is being given to mothers with children at school and to the elderly by offering appointments at appropriate times during the day.

Transport

Patients with their own transport

Many patients will attend both hospital and general practice by car and, although hospitals are now providing more car-parking facilities for all patients, special consideration should be given to the elderly or those with physical difficulties to provide parking as near as possible to the clinic they are attending.

Similarly, although doctors may not have the space to provide adequate parking for all patients, special consideration should be given to the elderly and patients with special needs to provide ease of access to health care.

Patients using public transport

Receptionists should be able to inform patients of local bus and train services, and to direct patients to the appropriate pick-up/drop-off points to enable them to reach their destinations. Information about local taxi services should also be available to patients.

Patients using the ambulance service

Receptionists should be aware of the categories of patients eligible for transport by ambulance to and from hospital (walking with assistance, sitting or stretcher cases). Eligibility is assessed by general practitioners or social services; receptionists will usually be asked by the GP to arrange appropriate transport for the patient's first visit to hospital. Subsequent transport for hospital attendance will either be arranged by the hospital receptionist or secretary, but may also be arranged directly by the hospital's ambulance service administrator.

Total quality in medical practice

The phrase 'total quality' is frequently used without any definition of what total quality actually means for the organization concerned.

NHS trusts, HAs and GPs are concerned with providing a quality service to their patients (customers) and many are committed to a total quality programme. An appropriate definition of total quality in providing health care might be:

A cost-effective system for integrating the continuous quality improve-ment efforts of all involved in health care to deliver services which ensure patient (customer) satisfaction.

Total quality strives to create a climate for excellence

Total quality strives to prevent errors rather than correct them

Total quality is based on effective and harmonious teamwork with absolute commitment of all members of the team

What is a doctor's view of quality?

What is the patient's view?

What is your view?

Patients want easy access to a doctor either in hospital or general prac-tice. They would like to wait in pleasant surroundings and want as short a waiting time as possible. They want a reasonable amount of time set aside for their consultation and expect receptionists and secretaries to smile, be sympathetic and responsive to their needs.

A doctor's perception of quality is probably very different, but they, too, expect an efficient service from their clerical staff as well as from the medical team in providing patient care.

Receptionists, secretaries, nurses and other members of the health team all have a different perception of quality. They cannot be expected to just provide an 'excellent' service while auditing themselves. They must be given the opportunity to share in the vision of what the organization is attempting to achieve. To do the job well, everyone will need guidelines; clear goals and objectives must be set and regular reviews and training given to help them create the climate for excellence.

Team members will be encouraged to set their own objectives and to monitor and improve their individual performance. They should be able to make suggestions for improved working methods and to discuss new ideas for improving the service.

Total quality is an extension of customer care, in which every receptionist and secretary working in the field of health care plays a vital role.

Audit and quality

Audit in health care may be defined as the monitoring and appraisal of performance against predetermined standards and targets to provide a quality service and care for the patient.

Summary

In this chapter we have looked at the contribution made by both receptionists and secretaries in the health service in their dealings with patients
and their role in creating the first impression that patients have of the
health care provided both in primary and secondary care.

Quality of health care provision and customer care go hand in hand to
achieve ever improving standards and patient satisfaction.

3

Communication

Introduction

Communication is the technical term for passing information. Effective communication is when appropriate information is not only passed on, but seen to be understood and acted upon. Therefore the skills of communication involve:

- listening and understanding what the patient/doctor requires
- conveying appropriate information
- checking that the information has been understood
- checking that a suitable response has been or will be made.

For the medical receptionist the responsibility of communicating with patients is:

to *listen* first

then give *appropriate* information

check by questioning that the patient understands

and *confirm* by observing whether action will be/has been taken whilst *maintaining confidentiality*

Listening

Listening does not merely involve hearing the words that are said, but also hearing what is not said, using intuition, common sense and reading behaviour to get the complete picture. On the telephone this is more difficult because body language (see Chapter 2) cannot be seen. However, it is important to tune into variations in tone of voice. With patients who are well known this will almost be an automatic process, but with people who are new it is even more important to exercise perception to get off to a good start.

The receptionist is the key person in ensuring that information is passed between patients, health care staff, hospitals, general practices, drug company representatives, pharmacists, suppliers and HA/health boards – to name but a few! It is vital that all the communication skills are used to best effect.

The receptionist needs to be skilled in all forms of communication – verbal, written form on paper, or by electronic means – but the majority of a receptionist's time will be spent in verbal communication.

DO	DON'T
Speak clearly	Eat or drink whilst speaking
One thing at a time – give 100% attention to each patient	Do two things at once, e.g. hunt for missing files, or work on the VDU whilst speaking to someone
Use words carefully	Use 'slang' or medical terms to patients
Control conversations with patients – use open and closed questions	Allow the patient to keep you longer than necessary
Be aware of your own tone of voice	Allow anger or frustration to show in your tone of voice

Use of questions in communicating

Awareness of the use of questions can help the receptionist to draw out patient needs or wrap up an unduly lingering conversation. Although a certain amount of questioning will be done automatically, or according to the practice/hospital policy, when difficulty is encountered using the right questions will help.

The simplest classification of questions is that they can be open, closed or leading.

- *Open* questions ease a patient into giving the information that is required, e.g. 'How can I help you ?' encourages the patient to state the need (for an appointment, result of test, etc.).

- *Leading* questions encourage a patient to make a decision by stating alternatives from which one needs to be selected, e.g. 'Do you want the appointment on Monday or Tuesday?' to which the logical answer is one of the two on offer, or 'You want to give up smoking, don't you?' to which the expected answer is 'Yes'.

- *Closed* questions bring the conversation to a halt, e.g. 'Shall I tell the doctor you need to speak to him?' to which the logical answer can only be 'Yes' or 'No'.

OPEN QUESTIONS begin with the words	CLOSED QUESTIONS begin with the words
When . . . .?	Would you . . . .?
How . . . .?	Shall I . . . .?
Who . . . .?	Are you . . . .?
What . . . .?	Do you . . . .?
Where . . . .?	May I . . . .?

Note: This is why 'May I help you?' is a poor way to address someone when you really want to help them, because the instant answer is either 'No', which is difficult for a British person to say outright to someone they do not know, or 'Yes' but does not help the person formulate their requirement!

Methods of communication

Communication is the way in which we transmit information, knowledge, thoughts and ideas from one person to another or to a group of people. In any organization, large or small, communication is important for the business to function effectively.

The four main methods of communication are:

- the spoken word (direct – face-to-face)

- the written word, e.g. diagrams, posters, notice boards etc.

- the use of telephone systems, including facsimile, answering machines, VDUs, E-mail, etc.

- Non-verbal communication (body language) (see Chapter 2).

Communication – internal and external

Communication may be either internal or external. The following are examples of written communication.

Written messages

Secretaries and receptionists are always conveying urgent and non-urgent messages from patients or other professionals. It is vital that the messages do not get mislaid and that appropriate action is taken. They should contain:

- the date and time the message is received

- the name, address and telephone number of the caller

- the name of the intended recipient of the message

- a clearly written and concise message

- the name, or initials, of the person taking the message.

Memorandum

A memorandum (memo) is an internal written communication which may be used to convey short messages and information to individuals or to all the health care team. Your organization will, no doubt, use a memorandum form which has several headings.

Notice boards

Notice boards can be used to convey information both internally to the organization or externally to visitors. Notice boards should be positioned so that they are readily visible and accessible to all who are expected to see the notices displayed. Notice boards should be kept up to date, and a member of the team will no doubt have responsibility for this.

White boards

These are often used in organizations to display information relevant to the day. Hospitals and surgeries may display notices about clinics running late, or health promotion information, etc.

Leaflets and posters

Hospitals and surgeries alike have access to a vast quantity of health promotion material and health messages to patients. Managers will often give responsibility to receptionists for displaying leaflets and posters, which should be shown to give impact to the intended message.

Protocols and procedures

All health care organizations will provide written protocols to communicate to members of the team the procedures for the activities in which staff are involved. Written protocols contain standards of quality and should be written so that all members of the team involved in the task fully understand the procedures and thus achieve objectives.

External written communication

Letters remain the most widely used method of written communication. Secretaries will be trained to provide a high standard of letter writing.

Letters are used to communicate with health authorities, NHS trusts, HAs, health boards, medical professionals and patients. For example, GPs write referral letters to hospital consultants; hospitals send discharge letters and reports to GPs.

Computers now provide a networking facility linking hospitals, HAs, laboratories and medical practices.

Report writing

Medical receptionists and secretaries may be asked to investigate a procedure or system that is not running smoothly, or to give an account of an event or incident which has occurred.

Reports are written on a given subject to:

- convey information and ideas

- sometimes to convey recommendations.

The features of a good report are that:

- it is easily understood

- it is always clear

- it is as long as it needs to be, but no longer.

A report must be complete and accurate with regard to the information it conveys and, because a decision may be based on the report, it must be correct.

A logical structure of the type of report you may be asked to present would be:

- introduction

    – subject heading or title

    – terms of reference – what you have been asked to find out

    – procedure – how you found out.

- body of report

    – findings – what you have found out.

- conclusion

    – conclusions – your conclusion or diagnosis

    – recommendations – what you think should be done.

Medical receptionists and secretaries may be asked to type more detailed reports, some of which may require a formal business format. There will, no doubt, be a 'house-style' which should be used, or reference to a manual of basic secretarial skills will give the necessary guidelines.

Note: A report must be accurate, clear, concise and logically arranged. It should be concise to the extent that there is no 'padding' or irrelevant details.

Telephone skills

Telephone callers only have tone of voice and words to go upon. Any frustrations felt at the time of answering the phone will be conveyed to the caller in the tone of voice and intonation on the words.

It is difficult to illustrate this point from the written word; however, consider the common phrase used by many organizations to answer the telephone: 'How can I help you?' This can be said with a genuine interest, conveyed by a warmth of tone. Alternatively, it can be said in a robotic tone which makes you, the caller, feel as though you want to leave a message on an answer machine for someone else to call back later!

Understandably, by 10.30 am on a busy Monday morning it may be difficult for a stressed receptionist to make an incoming caller feel 'welcome'. Difficult, but not impossible. It may be helpful to have some kind of personal motto to say to oneself at difficult times, e.g. 'Do as you would be done by', 'Speak as you would want to be spoken to'. Self control, conscious use of a warm tone of voice, and the personal motto are useful aids to ensuring the phone is answered to a consistently high standard.

Telephone enquiries

Secretaries and receptionists receive numerous telephone enquiries during the course of their day-to-day work. They may be typing lengthy reports, running a busy surgery or clinic or retrieving data from the computer, but the telephone enquiries and requests continue! Maintaining the balance between conflicting demands is part of the job, and the telephone caller should never have the impression that you are too flustered or annoyed at being interrupted and too busy to deal with their request.

- Answer the telephone as promptly as possible.

- Announce the practice or clinic, and give your name. (You will, no doubt, have your protocol for this.)

- Establish the caller's identity and try to help.

- If the caller is using a pay-phone, take the number and ring them back promptly if necessary.

- Politely ask the caller to hold if you need to deal with a visitor.

Golden rules when using the telephone

- Be polite.

- Do not eat while you are speaking on the telephone.

- Do not hold two conversations at the same time.

- Return to the caller every 30 seconds if you are keeping them on hold.

- If you are unable to help the caller yourself, track down someone who can – if necessary call them back.

People skills – face-to-face

In contrast to telephone communication where the only indicators are words and tone of voice, in a face-to-face encounter there is the additional dimension of 'non-verbal communication'. These are the signals that are given out and picked up, sometimes subconsciously, but which cause a reaction every bit as strong as to the words and tone. For example, a patient who is failing to get what they want is not only likely to raise their voice, but lean forwards over the reception counter. In response a receptionist could either spontaneously lean forward with a matching aggressive reaction, step back from the desk in a defensive manner, or calmly remain in the same position. Not only does the body move and thereby speak more clearly than our words, but the hands and face underline the expression of feeling. Hands may become clenched into fists and smiles disappear. With this knowledge in mind, the skill is to maintain self control and gain control of the situation. There are no set patterns of dealing with difficult situations, but attending courses, practice in role play, watching video clips, discussing situations after they have happened, watching colleagues and learning from their successes/weaknesses can all contribute to gaining experience and improving existing skills.

The medical receptionist or secretary also needs to constantly bear in mind the fact that patients are likely to not feel well, be anxious about what is going to be done to them, what the doctor may say, and concerned about the effect of their illness on the family. These feelings make patients stressed and therefore more sensitive to off-hand treatment. From the moment they are dealt with they need to feel that they are the one and only concern of the receptionist.

Recall good and bad experiences of how you have been made to feel in shops, offices, hospital, doctor's surgery

What made you feel bad?

What made you feel good?

What can you incorporate into your way of working to make patients feel as good as they can in the circumstances?

Meetings

Staff meetings, departmental or primary health care team meetings and patient participation groups are the type of meeting where receptionists and secretaries may be required to express a view. With modern management techniques meetings have become an important tool for communicating. They are the opportunity to find out what is going on, to be updated with the latest information and to contribute to forward planning. Even in a well-chaired, relatively informal meeting, staff who have every confidence in dealing with difficult patients at the desk may find it almost impossible to speak out in a meeting with doctors/managers present. The skill to speak out can be cultivated by practice, and helped by planning.

If you are going to be called upon to speak, prepare for the occasion

DO

Read the agenda circulated a few days before the meeting

Think about what you want to say

Write down a few key words

Define one statement that encapsulates your view succinctly

Make an outline of what you want to say

You should succeed in confidently making your point and gain respect not only for your view but for your ability to communicate

DON'T

Go into the meeting intending to say whatever comes into your head at the time

You may lose the opportunity to say what you really want to say, waste other people's time, and they may lose respect for you

---

Performance review

Receptionists and secretaries will no doubt be aware of other forms of 'communication' within their organizations, for example, performance review or 'appraisal' interviews, where he/she will be given the opportunity to communicate how they perceive their personal strengths and limitations, and perhaps identify areas where further training is needed.

Counselling

Counselling may be defined as: 'assisting individuals towards independence or self-actualization'. It is a form of communication designed to
enable employees to make their own decisions or choices. It involves:

- listening

- guiding

- communicating

- information giving.

Counselling is non-judgemental, it does not make assumptions, and can
be used to prevent a problem, or can help to work through an existing
problem.

The practice leaflet

Practice information leaflets communicate to patients the services available at the practice and how they may make better use of the primary
health care service. New patients will find the practice leaflet a valuable
source of information, not only about the services offered, but also regarding the members of the primary health care team, the times of the surgery
and clinic sessions and how to contact the doctor in an emergency.

Your practice leaflets should be attractively designed to make both
patients and potential patients aware of the services and quality of care
provided. They should be prominently positioned on the reception
counter and readily accessible to all callers.

Hospital information leaflets

NHS trusts and private hospitals and clinics will provide information
about the services which they offer. As well as basic information of hospital clinics, open access facilities and times of visiting, etc., they will give
details of transport to the hospital and car-parking provision.

Networking

Every organization is changing to a greater or lesser degree on a
regular basis. Staff come and go, the organizational structure changes,

responsibilities are shifted from one department to another. Therefore it is important that personal contacts are made and maintained so that if a receptionist/secretary does not know how to do something, or does not have a vital piece of information, then there is always someone to turn to, who will either know the answer themselves or 'know a man who does'. It is also important to keep up to date with the latest information by reading magazines as a vital supplement to networking.

Barriers to communication

Physical barriers

Physical barriers to communication may include the following:

- too much noise
- insufficient privacy
- frequent interruptions
- physical handicap, e.g. deafness, blindness or stammer
- the reception counter may be too high or too low
- telephone constantly ringing.

Receptionists'/secretaries' language

The language used when speaking to patients is a vital part of good communication. You must be aware of:

- using words (and 'jargon') that the patient cannot understand
- talking too quickly, or too quietly
- talking with a strong accent
- confusing patients by giving them too much information.

Patients' language

Patients from ethnic minorities may have difficulty in understanding and speaking the English language. You may have a colleague who can speak their language, or an interpreter may be necessary.

Psychological barriers

You must be aware of the psychological elements which may form barriers to good communication. Patients may find it difficult to communicate for the following reasons:

- feelings of inadequacy

- lacking in confidence

- emotionally upset by pain and/or anxiety about their medical condition

- unable to concentrate because of illness.

Attitudes of secretaries and receptionists

Remember the importance of positive non-verbal signs. A negative attitude will be a barrier to communication, for example:

- being impatient and rude

- not giving undivided attention

- appearing critical or demonstrating a superior attitude

- lack of eye contact

- appearing to be too busy

- feeling cross and under stress.

Attitudes of patients

An understanding of the reasons for patients' attitudes may help you to deal with them in a sympathetic manner and to overcome the barrier their attitude may present. For example they may be:

- too ill to concentrate

- resentful at having to present themselves at the reception desk

- terrified they have a serious illness

- afraid of appearing stupid to the efficient secretary or receptionist

- have a personal problem
- inhibited by finding they know the receptionist or secretary socially.

Overcoming the barriers

An awareness of the barriers combined with good common sense is a good start to overcoming any problems.

- Try to answer all questions in a positive way.
- A pleasant manner, a smile and understanding often does the trick – it is hard to be difficult when empathy is extended to you.
- Always be polite.
- Be alert to any problems which might occur.
- Always try to be helpful, smiling, calm and able to cope.
- If patients are kept waiting for longer than necessary, apologize, and give an explanation.
- When making appointments, ensure that the patients have the date and time written down to avoid any future misunderstanding.
- Try to give each patient your attention when dealing with them. Make eye contact, listen carefully to what they are saying.
- Never sound tired or bored, or look as if you are not listening.

Confidentiality

Remember that the rules of confidentiality that apply to working in any health care environment are as equally important when communicating with patients.

All information is privileged information, and *must not* be divulged without the doctor's prior consent.

4

Law, ethics and medicine

Introduction

The relationships between professional health care workers and between them and their patients are governed by the professional ethics and etiquette of medicine which have developed over the centuries together with developments in medicine itself. Secretaries and receptionists working closely with doctors and other health care workers, as well as being in constant communication with patients, should be aware of the important role of ethics and etiquette.

Ethics relate to moral principles and standards of what is morally right and wrong and are the guiding rules of professional behaviour. They are directed towards the benefit of the patients. *Etiquette* is concerned with the courtesy and politeness of normal behaviour.

History of ethics and etiquette

History shows that even from the earliest times, various legal systems have incorporated some degree of regulation of doctors. The earliest records were the Code of Laws of Hammurabi (1790 BC), when fees were regulated. Success was rewarded in accordance with the status of the patient, but failure was punished, frequently by mutilation.

The earliest record and declaration of ethics was made in the Hippocratic Oath (400 BC), which reflects the culture of the Hippocratic physicians. The standards expressed in the Hippocratic Oath, although no longer affirmed by today's physicians, is still accepted as the ideal of professional behaviour. (See Appendix 2.)

The Hippocratic Oath demonstrates the early concern of the profession to regulate itself by laying down basic standards of professional conduct, not only between doctor and patient, but also between teacher and pupil. For centuries thereafter, the principles of Christian humanism dominated the practice of medicine. Traditions of etiquette in public and private life gradually came about and, combined with the criteria of professional conduct, established the physician's position in society.

In 1798, the proposals of Sir Thomas Percival in Manchester ultimately became the 'Professional Conduct of Physicians and Surgeons', published in 1803. This laid the foundations for modern ethical standards in the UK.

The Provincial Medical and Surgical Association formed in 1832, which became the British Medical Association (BMA) in 1856, appointed a committee on medical ethics in 1849. This formed the basis of the General Ethical Committee of the BMA which has always played a leading role not only establishing ethical standards for the professional in the UK, but also for standards adopted as norms of conduct for doctors in many parts of the world.

The BMA was largely responsible for the establishment of the General Medical Council (GMC) under the Medical Act of 1858. The GMC has a regulatory role and from time to time issues guidance to members of the medical profession to enable them to avoid action which might lead to charges of professional misconduct. (The roles of both the BMA and GMC will be covered in more detail later in this chapter.)

Medical ethics and etiquette

Every medical receptionist and secretary must be aware of the important areas of ethical behaviour and etiquette. It has already been stated that ethics are directed towards the benefits of the patients, and many are bound into a code of conduct published by the GMC for doctors, and by other regulatory bodies for other health professionals, for example:

- General Dental Council – Dentists

- General Nursing Council – Nurses.

All regulatory bodies have the responsibility of maintaining the register of those allowed to practise as a doctor, dentist, nurse, etc. The ultimate sanction on those judged to have behaved unethically is the removal of their name from the register, and thus the removal of the ability to practise.

There are no formal sanctions for those in breach of etiquette, but the rules have been established by custom. They aid communication between professionals and avoid damaging reputations, so they may be said to indirectly benefit patients.

A modern restatement of the Hippocratic Oath was formulated by the World Medical Association in 1947 to reflect the changing attitudes of society and major advances in medical science. It is known as the Declaration of Geneva:

> I solemnly pledge myself to consecrate my life to the service of human-ity;
> I will give to my teachers the respect and gratitude which is their due;
> I will practise my profession with dignity;
> The health of my patient will be my first consideration;
> I will respect the secrets which are confided in me, even after the patient has died;
> I will maintain by all the means of my power, the honour and the noble traditions of the medical profession;
> My colleagues will be my brothers;
> I will not permit considerations of religion, nationality, race, party poli-tics or social standing to intervene between me and my patients;
> I will maintain the utmost respect for human life from the time of con-ception; even under threat I will not use my medical knowledge contrary to the laws of humanity;
> I make these promises solemnly, freely and upon my honour.

There are four important areas of ethical behaviour and etiquette that all secretaries and receptionists in medical practice should be aware of and should apply the principles of to their day-to-day work:

- confidentiality

- trust

- confidence

- integrity.

Confidentiality

Confidentiality places a constraint upon all those who work in the field of health care. The terms and conditions of employment of medical secre-taries and receptionists, wherever employed, will almost certainly contain a clause to the effect that any breach of confidentiality will result in disci-plinary action, even dismissal; they will, no doubt, be asked to sign state-ments signifying that this is fully understood.

The Declaration of Geneva maintains that a doctor must preserve secrecy in all he knows – even after the death of his patient. However, there are certain exceptions to this:

- when the patient gives consent

- when it is undesirable on medical grounds to seek a patient's consent, but it is in the patient's best interests that confidentiality should be broken

- the doctor's overriding duty to society

- for the purposes of medical research, when approved by a local clinical research ethical committee, or in the case of the National Cancer Registry by the Chairman of the BMA's Central Ethical Committee.

Doctors must be able to justify their decisions to disclose information. A doctor must ensure, as far as possible, that all medical information is kept in a secure place.

Confidentiality and medical records

Secretaries and receptionists are in the privileged position of having access to medical records which contain confidential information about patients and they should always remember that patients trust doctors not to divulge any personal information contained in the record. Likewise, confidential information should never be discussed or divulged by secretaries or receptionists.

Discretion is necessary when dealing with enquiries from solicitors, relatives or representatives of the patient, and insurance companies. Staff should always be circumspect when they deal with patients. When speaking with colleagues, great care should be taken. Some hospitals insist that patients are referred to by their hospital number and not by name.

Secretaries and receptionists working in a hospital will usually find that their medical records manager will require them to sign a form stating that they understand the legal and ethical aspects of confidentiality and that any behaviour contravening this may result in termination of employment.

Any information contained in medical records may only be disclosed in certain circumstances.

Trust

Doctors as part of their work in dealing with patients and their families are entrusted with information that would not be divulged to others. Good medical practice is based on the maintenance of trust between doctors, patients and their families with the knowledge that professional relationships will be strictly observed. Not only doctors, but medical secretaries and receptionists must at all times exercise care and discretion to maintain this special relationship.

Confidence

Confidence like trust is also vitally important in the doctor/patient relationship. Staff should appreciate that if patients have been helped by a doctor on a previous occasion, they are confident they will be helped in any further episodes. Whilst this may make the doctor's task easier, it also places added responsibility on the doctor – doctors know they cannot always succeed.

Integrity

Doctors will act professionally and objectively in the best interests of their patients in their judgements and patient care. Receptionists and staff also should behave in a professional manner and remain circumspect at all times. Considerable pressure is placed on doctors and health care staff, for example pressures from relatives, advertising, the media, etc. It is, perhaps, worth considering the duties of a doctor and rights of patients in the context of ethics and etiquette in medicine.

Doctors' duties

At the end of 1996, the GMC published *Duties of a Doctor*, describing good medical practice and giving guidance on the duties of doctors registered with the GMC. Patients must be able to trust doctors with their lives and well-being. To justify that trust they as a profession have a duty to maintain a good standard of practice and care and to show respect for human life. In particular, doctors must:

- make the care of their patients their first concern
- treat every patient politely and considerately
- respect patients' dignity and privacy
- listen to patients and respect their views
- give patients information in a way they can understand
- respect the rights of patients to be fully involved in decisions about their care
- keep their professional knowledge and skills up-to-date
- recognize the limits of their professional competence
- be honest and trustworthy

- respect and protect confidential information
- make sure their personal beliefs do not prejudice their patients' care
- act quickly to protect patients from risk if they have good reason to believe that they or a colleague may not be fit to practice
- work with colleagues in the ways that best serve patients' interests.

In all these matters, doctors must never discriminate against their patients or colleagues, and must always be prepared to justify their actions to them.

Overall management

It is good medical practice for one doctor to be responsible for the overall management of a patient's illness.

Referral from a GP to a consultant has evolved in the patient's interest. A consultant or specialist should not accept a patient without referral from a GP. There are exceptions, e.g. sexually transmitted diseases, family planning and casualty.

Consent to treatment

The patient's trust that their consent to treatment will not be misused is an essential part of their relationship with their doctor; for a doctor even to touch a patient without consent is an assault. Doctors offer advice, but it is the patient who decides whether or not to accept the advice. The onus is on the doctor to explain in such a way that advice will be accepted.

Patients' rights

Patients have certain rights in relation to their use of health care services. These rights generally fall into two categories:

1   the right to treatment
2   the right to confidentiality.

The right to treatment

A patient:

- has the right to be on a GP's list of patients

- has the right to see a GP (not necessarily their own) at the GP's surgery at any time during surgery hours

- should have access to a telephone number at which a GP can be reached 24 hours a day, 365 days a year

- should be visited at home if it is considered necessary by the GP

- must receive any treatment which is immediately necessary when temporarily away from home

- has the right to change GPs without giving a reason by applying to another GP

- has no absolute right to a second opinion, but the doctor should take reasonable care to seek one if they are unsure of the diagnosis or treatment

- needs to give consent before being examined or treated

- is not legally bound to accept treatment. However, doctors can give essential treatment if the patient is temporarily incapable of understanding or consenting to treatment, e.g. through alcohol or drugs. If the patient is permanently incapable through mental illness it is possible for a legal guardian to give consent

- has the right to refuse to be examined with a medical student present

- has the right to a full and truthful reply to any specific question unless the information may result in anxiety which may injure the patient's health

- has the right to see and amend medical records made on or after 1 November 1991, unless they will cause harm to the patient. (See Access to Health Records Act 1990.) Hospitals, private clinics, GP practices, etc. who hold patient information on computer have to follow the Data Protection Act which protects patients' rights (Data Protection Act 1984)

- has the right to complain about their doctor if they have not followed their terms of service or if a doctor behaves in an unethical manner.

The right to confidentiality

Doctors must not pass on information without the patient's consent except to those involved in the treatment and care or, when it is in the best interests of the patient, to close relatives. The law requires doctors to give information about patients to health and other authorities in certain circumstances:

- when ordered by a court
- if the patient has certain infectious diseases or food poisoning
- if they suspect the patient is addicted to a hard drug
- if they arrange an abortion for a patient
- if required by the police to help identify a driver suspected of motoring offences.

Chaperoning

All too frequently we hear about doctors accused of indecently assaulting their patients, and doctors today are at risk from such accusations. The presence of a third person as a chaperone, usually a nurse, is a valuable insurance for the practitioner. However, there may be occasions when the doctor's secretary or receptionist will be asked to be present at the consultation, particularly in private practice when a nurse is not always available.

If the patient is emotionally upset or mentally disturbed when consulting a doctor, the presence of a chaperone not only protects the doctor, but may also relieve the patient of some embarrassment and anxiety.

The regulatory bodies and their role

The General Medical Council

The General Medical Council (GMC) was established under the Medical Act of 1858 with the purpose of distinguishing between unqualified practitioners or 'quacks' and the qualified medical practitioner. The Medical Register was thus established, with records of medical practitioners and their qualifications.

One of the most important functions of the GMC is to protect patients and to guide doctors.

Functions of the GMC

- To keep a register of all medical practitioners who have obtained qualifying degrees, giving them licence to practise. The GMC publishes this register, providing the public with the names of doctors who have acquired the necessary medical qualifications and experience to equip them to practise in the UK.

- To keep a separate register of those practitioners who have obtained higher degrees.

- The GMC sets out standards of medical education.

- It is responsible for the publication of the British Pharmacopoeia (BP).

- The GMC has an important regulatory role; it issues guidelines to all members of the medical profession to enable them to avoid actions which might lead to charges of professional misconduct.

- It has a duty to administer discipline. It is to the GMC that the public and medical profession may make complaints about a doctor's behaviour.

- The GMC has the power, if such a charge is proved, to temporarily suspend a doctor from practising or, if necessary, to remove their name ('struck-off') from the register.

Health procedures

In addition to conduct procedures, the GMC's health procedures look into the cases of doctors who are suffering from illnesses affecting their ability to practise medicine safely. These illnesses are almost invariably alcohol or drug-related or a mental condition. The health procedures not only protect the public but also offer doctors expert medical supervision and support.

Performance procedures

In September 1997, the GMC's powers were extended to cover a third set of procedures to take action against incompetent doctors who represent a danger to their patients. Doctors referred to these procedures will have their professional performance assessed by teams of medical and lay assessors – the Committee on Professional Performance. If it is deemed appropriate, doctors will be asked to accept further training or counselling to remedy their deficiencies before an act of serious professional misconduct occurs.

Doctors whose performance is considered to be a serious risk to the public, or who are unwilling or unable to be retrained, will face a private hearing with the possibility of their registration being restricted or suspended.

The British Medical Association

The British Medical Association (BMA) was founded in 1832 by Charles Hastings and is the largest medical association in the UK. It is concerned with most aspects of medicine and is one of the principal bodies representing British doctors.

The BMA played an important part in the establishment of the General Medical Council. The Central Ethical Committee of the BMA plays a leading role in establishing ethical standards for the medical profession in the UK, and also for the standards which have been adopted as norms of conduct for doctors throughout the world.

Medical science is advancing so rapidly and, with new discoveries being communicated to the public, the BMA issues ethical guidelines to reflect and safeguard the well-being and interests of patients, and, at the same time, expressing the views of the profession on medical ethics.

Summary of medical ethics and etiquette

In looking at the ethics and etiquette of medical practice, the receptionist or secretary will understand that patients not only expect doctors to use their expertise and skill, but also to observe absolute confidentiality regarding any information imparted as a result of the consultation, examination and treatment. On this understanding of professional confidence and secrecy, all those working in the field of health care will be aware of the special relationship which exists between doctor and patient.

Having considered the various ethical issues that confront the medical profession, and the role of the regulatory bodies, we are able to appreciate the problems facing doctors and their ability to resolve the numerous ethical and moral dilemmas that may arise. These include:

- abortion
- euthanasia
- screening
- genetic counselling

- artificial insemination
- severely malformed infants
- in vitro fertilization
- consent to operations on reproductive organs
- HIV/AIDS.

Practical considerations for secretaries and receptionists

- Remember that your work is strictly confidential – anything that is divulged by a patient to the doctor, the medical records or correspondence must not be disclosed to anyone else.

- Details of your work or personal affairs of doctors and other health care professionals must *not* be discussed.

- The behaviour of, or treatment by, a medical practitioner or any professional health care worker must *not* be openly criticized within hearing distance of the patient.

- Always be circumspect when talking about a doctor or other health care professional to another person. Do not unduly praise or criticize their accomplishments.

- It is your responsibility to facilitate the doctor's treatment and care of their patients.

Legal aspects

Medical secretaries and receptionists, although not needing detailed knowledge of law, should have an understanding of those legal aspects affecting their day-to-day work.

Patient access to information

Over the past decade patients and carers have had an increasing expectation of access to information about their own health care, and this trend has been encouraged by NHS policy. There are very good reasons for giving patients access. First, it is ethical to do so as truth telling is not only a moral absolute but also produces a relationship based on mutual trust. Second, there is abundant evidence that people want more information about their own health care and treatment, and clinical trials have demonstrated that improved functional and health status is connected to good doctor–patient information sharing. Third, legislation requires that patients should have access to information and rights to information in the UK have, since 1991, been set out in the Patient's Charter, which summarizes the rights and standards based on both legislation and common law. The right of access to health records was established by two acts of parliament:

- The Data Protection Act 1984
- Access to Health Records Act 1990.

More recently, new agendas have emphasized the need for improved patient access to information, including:

- Purchasing Intelligence and Local Voice
- NHS Code of Openness
- Patient Partnership Strategy
- Promoting Clinical Effectiveness
- NHS Research and Development.

There is an increasing awareness that sharing information with patients, carers and the wider public can be a significant factor in encouraging informed and discerning use of health services. Sharing information also encourages professionals to develop skills in communicating with patients.

The NHS Code of Openness (published in 1995) encourages both purchasers and providers to enable public access to information about NHS services, costs, quality and performance, proposed service changes and how to influence decisions, decisions and actions affecting their own treatment, and what information is available and how to get it. There has been a recent noticeable growth in information services for patients and the public. Under the Patient's Charter, a single national freephone number for health information was established and Health Service Guidelines required local centres to provide information on:

- common illnesses and treatments
- self-help groups
- waiting times
- health care services
- keeping healthy
- patients' rights and how to complain
- Patient's Charter standards.

Medical Records

Hospitals, general practice and any health care organization recording information on computer about identifiable living individuals must ensure that the provisions of the Data Protection Act are complied with.

The Data Protection Act 1984

The Data Protection Act is designed and based on principles to ensure that information relating to an individual is obtained fairly, kept up to date and stored securely. Individuals, whose data are stored, have rights of access enabling them to check the accuracy of the information. The data protection registrar and the courts are empowered to require correction of inaccurate material if it is not undertaken voluntarily by the data user.

The medical context of the individual's right of access to information held about him/her has been modified by the Data Protection (Subject Access Modification) (Health) Order 1987. This allows information to be withheld from an individual if it is likely to cause serious harm to his or her mental or physical health, or discloses the identity of another person other than the health care professional. A doctor who withholds information must be prepared to justify their actions in a court if challenged at a later date. This Act applies to England, Wales, Scotland and Northern Ireland.

The Access to Medical Reports Act 1988

This Act establishes an individual's right of access to medical reports prepared for insurance or employment purposes, by doctors who either are, or have been, responsible for that person's care. The Act applies only to England, Wales and Scotland, but similar provisions now apply to Northern Ireland under the Access to Personal Files and Medical Reports Order 1991.

At the same time that the patient's consent to the preparation of the report is obtained, the commissioning company is required to inform the individual of his/her rights under the Act, and to enquire whether access to the report is required. The information is passed on to the doctor.

If the patient requires access, he/she is allowed 21 days to make appropriate arrangements to view the report. Patients who originally declined the opportunity of access may make application to see the report until the time it is despatched to the company and, if so, must be allowed 21 days to make appropriate arrangements.

Once the report has been seen by the patient, he/she may agree to the despatch unaltered, request correction of factual accuracy or, where the doctor declines to make the requested correction, append a statement of his/her own, or may refuse to allow the report to be released.

The Access to Health Records Act 1990

This Act applies to England, Wales and Scotland and has established a right of access for patients to whom the records relate and, in certain circumstances, to other individuals. The Act also makes provision for correction of inaccurate records.

Under the Act, a health record is any record containing information relating to the physical or mental health of an individual who can be identified from that information which has been made by 'or on behalf of' a health care professional.

Applications for access must be made in writing to the record holder and, provided no addition to the record has been made within the previous 40 days, a fee may be charged. Provided there is no reason to withhold access, the record holder must allow the applicant to see the records within 40 days, unless the most recent note has been made within 40 days, in which case the time limit is 21 days. If a copied set of the medical record is required, a copying and postal charge may be made. Applications may be made by the patient or someone appointed on the patient's behalf:

- in the case of a child, the parent or guardian

- in the case of an incapable patient, a person appointed by the court to manage their affairs

- after a patient's death, by the patient's personal representatives or anyone who might have a claim arising out of the patient's death.

The Law and Mental Health

Mental Health Act

Secretaries and receptionists working in the field of health care will need an understanding of the implications of the law relating to mental illness.

The law has changed with the Mental Health Act of 1983. The provisions of this Act are of particular importance to those patients who are compulsorily detained under the Act. This involves approximately 10% of all patients who are admitted to psychiatric hospitals or departments.

The Mental Health Act of 1983 established the Mental Health Act Commission which has a responsibility to protect the rights of detained patients and to keep under review the exercise of compulsory power and duties conferred by the Act. The Act also provides the legal instrument which enables society to act in the interests of, and on behalf of, patients and those convicted of certain criminal offences, who are diagnosed as having certain abnormal mental conditions, and makes provision for the protection of the public, and for the protection of the property of patients compulsorily detained.

The primary concerns of the 1983 Mental Health Act are:

- protection of the mentally sick person

- protection of his/her property

- protection of the public.

The Act defines certain relevant legal mental conditions as follow.

- *Mental disorder* which means illness, arrested or incomplete development of mind, psychopathic disorder and any other disorder or disability of mind.

- *Severe mental impairment* which means a state of arrested or incomplete development of intelligence and social functions, and is associated with abnormally aggressive or seriously irresponsible conduct on the part of the person concerned.

- *Mental impairment* which means a state of arrested or incomplete development of mind (not amounting to severe mental impairment) which includes significant impairment of intelligence and social functioning and is associated with abnormally aggressive or seriously irresponsible conduct on the part of the person concerned.

- *Psychopathic disorder* which means a persistent disorder or disability of mind (whether or not including significant impairment of intelligence) which results in abnormally aggressive or seriously irresponsible conduct on the part of the person concerned.

A person may not be regarded as suffering from mental disorder by reason only of promiscuity or other immoral conduct, sexual deviancy or dependence on alcohol or drugs.

The legislation emphazises:

1 As much treatment as possible on a voluntary basis, both in hospital and in the home or other institution.
2 A shift from institutional care to care within the home as far as possible.
3 Proper provision for those to be detained on a compulsory basis in the interests of the patient and society.

Medical secretaries and receptionists will from time to time be involved in arrangements for patient admission, either formally or informally, to undergo psychiatric treatment. Such admissions come within sections of the Mental Health Act. A brief outline of admission under some of the sections of the Mental Health Act is given on the following page.

Methods by which a person may enter a hospital for psychiatric treatment

Informal admission (Section 131)

Any person having attained the age of 16 may request admission, or a person under the age of 16 where the parent or guardian gives consent, or any person to whom it is suggested that admission is advisable and that person does not refuse, can be admitted without any legal formalities. This patient can discharge him/herself unless the doctor in charge decides that if discharged he/she would be endangering his/her health or safety or that of others.

Compulsory admission and detention

The following methods of admission can be used when a person suffering from mental disorder as defined by the Act is in need of psychiatric care but is not prepared to enter hospital or remain in hospital for observation or treatment.

- *Section 2: (up to 28 days)* – Admission for assessment (or for assessment followed by medical treatment).
  An application for the admission of the patient must be made either by an approved social worker or the nearest relative, plus a medical recommendation from one 'psychiatrist' and a doctor (if practicable one doctor should have previous acquaintance of the patient, for example, his/her GP). The person making the application should have seen the patient within the last 14 days.

- *Section 3: (up to 6 months)* – Detention for treatment.
  The application for detention under Section 3 is the same as for Section 2, except that the approved social worker is not to act if the nearest relative objects. This section can be reviewed for a further six months, and yearly thereafter.

  Note: Patients may apply to the Mental Health Review Tribunal (NHRT) under Sections 2 and 3, subject to the stated criteria.

- *Section 4: (up to 72 hours)* – Admission for assessment.
  The application must be made either by an approved social worker or the nearest relative, plus a recommendation from a medical practitioner who must have seen the patient within the last 24 hours. The patient must arrive at the hospital within 24 hours of the medical examination. (This may be converted into Section 2 if a second medical recommendation is received within 72 hours.)

Consent to treatment

Certain sections (56–64) of the Mental Health Act are largely concerned with consent to treatment for long-term detained patients, but certain safeguards also apply to informal patients.

The Mental Health (Patients in the Community) Act 1995

The Mental Health (Patients in the Community) Act 1995, which came into force on 1 April 1996, introduced a new power of supervised discharge available in the case of unrestricted patients who, in the opinion of the responsible medical officer, are ready to leave hospital but, because of the risk they present to themselves or others, need special support to live safely in the community. The patient's care plan, which must be in place before an application for supervised discharge is made, may include formal requirements such as attendance for rehabilitation or treatment or the requirement to live at a particular residence. A named supervisor and responsible medical officer will be identified. Non-compliance will lead to an immediate review and possible compulsory re-admission.

Care Programme Approach

The Care Programme Approach (CPA) is one of the cornerstones of policy on mental health, providing a framework for the care of mentally ill people which ensures that services are targeted to people with severe mental health problems.

Building Bridges

This paper published in November 1996, offers detailed advice and guidance on arrangements for effective, co-ordinated, inter-agency work for the care and protection of severely mentally ill people.

Patients in the community – future trends

In January 1998, the Health Secretary announced that the Government would replace the practice of sending mentally ill patients out into the community with a mixture of hospital and community provision, which would provide more appropriate supervision. The Health Secretary felt that severely disturbed patients should be kept in secure units to protect the public.

It is expected that the Labour Government will introduce a Mental Incapacity Bill to implement the changes which would undoubtedly lead to the recall into residential care of some patients now living in unsupervised units.

Employment law

There are a number of laws influencing the employment of staff. It is important that all employees, including medical secretaries and receptionists, understand their rights.

From the point when a verbal offer of a job has been made and the post accepted, the formal contract comes into being. At this stage nothing further is required to signify its existence and both parties are bound by it from that point on. However, to avoid any misunderstanding, employers will generally follow up a job offer and acceptance with a letter.

Written statement of main terms and conditions

Employers are required to provide employees working eight hours or more each week with a written statement of the main terms and conditions of their employment within two months of starting. This was not the case prior to 1993, but if any such staff who were appointed before this date ask for a statement, they must be given one within two months of asking. All staff must be given notification of any changes to specified terms and conditions when they occur.

The written statement must contain:

- the employer's name

- the employee's name

- starting date of employment

- date continuous service began and whether or not employment with another employer (other hospital or medical practice) is counted

- job title

- rate of pay

- payment intervals (monthly, weekly)

- hours of work

- place of work

- holiday entitlement and holiday pay.

The following additional information must also be provided within the two-month period (as part of the principal statement or separately):

- sick leave and sick pay

- pension scheme

- notice periods on either side

- end date of a fixed-term contract, or likely end date of a temporary one

- particulars of collective agreements where these apply (e.g. as agreed by Whitley Council)

- grievance procedure and to whom a grievance can be raised

- disciplinary rules and procedures, and to whom appeals can be made – this applies only to employers of 20 or more staff.

Sometimes relevant information relating to sickness, pensions, grievances, disciplinary rules, procedures and appeals is kept in separate reference documents. In this case, the written statement will refer to these; they should be readily accessible to employees in the course of their work.

Equality of opportunity

We discriminate between people both in the workplace and in day-to-day life. Some forms of discrimination are acceptable, but others are not, and certain forms have been determined to be unlawful. Legislation relating to equality of opportunity requires employers to exercise some form of social responsibility in making decisions about employees, current or potential. Employees, too, may unconsciously discriminate between people; we are not always aware of how our prejudices and preconceptions colour our judgement and the way we deal with others.

Equality can only be achieved through an acceptance by all members of the work team that it is important, in their own interests and in the interests of the service they provide.

Equal opportunities legislation

Equality of opportunity regardless of sex, race, marriage, disablement, religion or age is vitally important, not only for employees to have a fair/equal chance of developing their potential abilities and realizing their expectations, but also for employers to make full and effective use of their staff and to improve employee relations. This legislation forbids discrimination between men and women with regard to pay and other terms in their contracts, for example:

- *Equal Pay Act 1970 and Equal Pay (Amendments) Regulations 1983*

    – overtime
    – bonus payments
    – holiday and sick pay entitlements.

- *Rehabilitation of Offenders Act 1974*

This Act allows an individual who has had a conviction for an offence to put it behind them and be rehabilitated after a period of time. Their conviction becomes 'spent' and they may lawfully conceal it from a prospective employer, as if it had never happened. However, certain exemptions exist.

- *Sex Discrimination Act 1975*

The Act describes direct discrimination as occurring if, on the grounds of her sex, a woman is treated less favourably than a man would be treated.

- *The Race Relations Act 1976*

The Act forbids racial discrimination in employment. It states that no person should treat another less favourably on racial grounds.

- *Disability Discrimination Act 1996*

The Act provides protection against discrimination to those who can show that they have a physical or mental impairment which has a substantial and long-term effect on their day-to-day activities. Employers are expected to make reasonable adjustments to the working environment where these will alleviate the disadvantages or risks faced by the handicapped employees or prospective employees. In cases of discrimination, Tribunals or County Courts can award compensation. There is no compensation limit.

General responsibilities under these Acts

Hospitals, medical practices, etc. have a legal obligation to ensure that they and their employees do not discriminate unlawfully.

All supervisory staff are responsible for eliminating any sexual harassment, victimization or intimidation of which they are aware.

Individual employees are expected to co-operate with measures designed to ensure equal opportunities and avoid unlawful discrimination. They should be encouraged to report incidents of harassment, victimization and pressure to discriminate where these occur.

Sexual harassment

Sexual harassment is judged as unlawful behaviour contrary to the Sex Discrimination Act 1974. Examples of sexual harassment are:

- unwanted physical conduct
- requests for sexual favours

- unwelcome sexual advances
- continued suggestions for social activity outside of work after it has been made clear that such suggestions are not welcome
- offensive flirtation, suggestive remarks, etc.
- the display of pornographic or sexually suggestive pictures, etc.
- leering, whistling or making sexually suggestive gestures
- derogatory or degrading abuse or insults which are gender related
- offensive comments about appearance or dress.

Certification

All doctors, whether working in private practices or in an NHS organization are requested from time to time to issue certificates, including:

- National Insurance/DSS certificates
- death certificates
- cremation certificates
- private medical or insurance certificates
- certificates of stillbirth.

Certification is a statutory obligation imposed upon doctors, and the secretary or receptionist should do all they can to ensure that the doctor is not placed in the position of being asked to improperly certify.

For example the doctor must always see the patient when issuing and signing the form on which a patient claims sickness benefit – Form Med 3 (Figures 4.1 and 4.2). This should not be issued more than one day after examination as the doctor has to certify that they have examined the patient today/yesterday.

Death certificates

The death certificate is the oldest of all official medical forms and is issued only to registered practitioners. The certificate is obtained from the registrar for the subdistrict in which the doctor practises. The issue of death certificates is a statutory requirement and no fee is chargeable. The

FOR SOCIAL SECURITY AND STATUTORY SICK PAY PURPOSES ONLY

<u>**NOTES TO PATIENT ABOUT USING THIS FORM**</u>

You can use this form either:

1.   For Statutory Sick Pay (SSP) purposes - fill in Part A overleaf. Also fill in Part B if the doctor has given you a date to resume work. Give or send the completed form to your employer.

2.   For Social Security purposes -
To continue a claim for state benefit fill in Parts A and C of the form overleaf. Also fill in Part B if the doctor has given you a date to resume work. **Sign and date the form and give or send it to your Local Social Security Office QUICKLY to avoid losing benefit.**

NOTE: To start your claim for State benefit you must use form SC1 if you are self-employed, unemployed or non-employed OR form SSP1 if you are an employee. For further details get leaflet NI16 (from Social Security Local Offices).

Doctor's Statement

In confidence to

Mr/Mrs/Miss/Ms ....

I examined you today/yesterday and advised you that

(a) You need not   (b) you should refrain from work
refrain from
work   for*†..

OR until ....

Diagnosis of your disorder
causing absence from work ....
Doctor's remarks

Doctor's   Date of
signature   signing

Form Med 3

NOTE TO DOCTOR*†   *See inside front cover for notes on completion*

Printed in the UK for HMSO 03/94 D.8444690 C50.000. 36625. (T3453)

Figure 4.1   Form Med 3 (sample).

if you cannot fill this in yourself ask someone to do so and sign it for you.

A.   TO BE COMPLETED IN ALL CASES - PLEASE USE BLOCK LETTERS

Surname Mr/Mrs/Miss/Ms

First names

Present address

Postcode

	Date	Month	Year
Date of birth			

National Insurance
Number

Works or Clock Number
or Department

B.   If the doctor has given you a date to resume work

Date you intend to start
(or seek) work for any
employer or as a self-
employed person

	Date	Month	Year
day			

For night shift
workers only

Shift will begin at   Time   am/pm

and end next day at   Time   am/pm

C.   FOR STATE BENEFIT CLAIMANTS ONLY

Full name and address
of employer (if employed)

DECLARATION

I understand that if I give incorrect or incomplete information action may be taken against me.

I declare that because of incapacity I have not worked since the date of my last claim.

I also declare that my circumstances and those of my dependants are and have been as last stated. (If there has been a change cross out this declaration and attach a signed and dated statement of new facts.)

I declare that the information I have given on this form is correct and complete.

I agree that a doctor acting on behalf of the Department of Social Security may get in touch with my doctor so that they may give the Department of Social Security any information which is needed to deal with this claim and any request to look at the claim again.

Signature .... Date ....

If you have signed this form for someone else
please tick here

Figure 4.1   Continued

**FOR SOCIAL SECURITY AND STATUTORY
SICK PAY PURPOSES ONLY**

**Special Statement
by the Doctor**

In confidence to
Mr/Mrs/Miss/Ms ....

(A) I examined you on the

following dates ....

....

....

and advised you that you
should refrain from work

from .... to ....

(B) I have not examined you but, on the basis of
a recent written report from –

Doctor .... (Name if known)

of ....

....

.... (Address)
I have advised you that you should refrain

from work for/until ....

Diagnosis of your disorder
causing absence from work ....

Doctor's remarks

Doctor's
signature

Date of
signing

*The special circumstances in which this form may be used are described in the
handbook "Medical Evidence for Social Security and Statutory Sick Pay Purposes".*

*Form Med 5
3/83*

PATIENT TO COMPLETE PARTICULARS ON REVERSE

Figure 4.2   Form Med 5.

TO BE COMPLETED IN ALL CASES – PLEASE USE BLOCK LETTERS
If you cannot fill this form in yourself, ask someone else to do so

Surname Mr/Mrs/Miss/Ms

First names

Present address

Postcode

Date of birth | Date | Month | Year

National insurance number

Works or clock number
or department

If the doctor has given you a date to resume work
date you intend to start (or | Date | Month | Year
seek) work for an employer | day
or as a self-employed person

For night shift workers only | Shift will begin at | Time | am/pm
| and end next day at | Time | am/pm

FOR STATE BENEFIT CLAIMANTS ONLY
If you wish to claim benefit, continue below. To avoid losing benefit send this form QUICKLY to your local Social Security Office.
NOTE: To start your claim for State benefit you must use form SC1 (Rev) if you are self-employed, unemployed or non-employed OR form SSP1(E) or SSP1(T) if you are an employee. For further details get leaflet N16 (from DHSS local offices).

Full name and address
of employer (if employed)

| DECLARATION |

Remember: if you give information that is incorrect or incomplete action may be taken against you.

I declare that because of incapacity I have not worked since the date of my last claim. I also declare that my circumstances and those of my dependants are and have been as last stated. (If there has been a change cross out this declaration and attach a signed and dated statement of new facts).

I declare that the information I have given is correct and complete.

I claim benefit.

I agree to my doctor giving medical information relevant to my claim to a doctor in the Regional Medical Service.

**Sign
here** .... Date ....

If you have signed on behalf of the person
claiming tick the box.

Printed in the UK for HMSO 7/87 Dd. 8080423 C 2,550 (11037).

Figure 4.2   Continued

certificate is given by a doctor who was actually attending the patient in their last illness, and where there is sufficient knowledge of the cause of death to do so. Doctors are bound by law to provide the certificate in a sealed envelope. The death certificate should be taken to the Registrar of Births and Deaths in the subdistrict of occurrence within five days of death.

There is no legal duty to notify the coroner of any death but, of course, this does not imply that the doctor need not do so when the circumstances require such action. Moral, ethical and traditional considerations necessitate that the doctor acts with responsibility and, by notifying the coroner, facilitates any enquiry into the death as the coroner deems advisable.

Role of medical secretary or receptionist

Secretaries and receptionists must appreciate the situation that when dealing with grieving relatives, sympathy, understanding and patience may be required. They should ensure that the death certificate is available when required, and clearly explain what the relatives/representatives should do with it; for example, taking it to the registrar's office within the statutory time, and, if necessary, give them directions.

Cremation certificates

Doctors may be requested to sign cremation certificates for patients they have attended during their last illness. Cremation certificates require confirmation by another doctor. Two signatures are always necessary, and a doctor may be asked to sign in either capacity. These certificates are available from local funeral directors, and the secretary/receptionist may be asked to ensure that there are forms available when required. A fee is payable to both signatories.

Private certification

Private certificates are issued to patients for purposes outside the scope of the NHS. They are used to supply information to organizations regarding proof of illness, for example:

* holiday insurance

* sick pay and superannuation purposes

* solicitors

- insurance companies
- schools.

A fee may be charged for private certificates. The BMA make recommendations of fees, and doctors will charge according to their recommended scale.

Certificate of stillbirth

A doctor must sign a certificate of stillbirth if they were present at the delivery or examined the body of a stillborn child, and give it to the person who will inform the registrar.

Birth registration

Every live or stillbirth must be registered within 42 days. It is the duty of either of the parents to register the birth. In the case of an illegitimate child, the duty to register the birth rests on the mother.

All certificates should either be stamped with the doctor's name, address etc., or may be printed in the case of a private certificate.

The Local Medical Officer must be notified of all births, either by the hospital or the doctor in attendance.

Abortion certificates

The law in Britain allows doctors to terminate pregnancies as long as certain conditions are met.

1   Two doctors must see the patient.
2   They must agree that the conditions laid down in the 1967 Abortion Act have been satisfied.

Note: Conditions allow doctors to recommend termination when they feel that to continue with the pregnancy would be a hazard to either the physical or mental welfare of the pregnant woman or any existing children of her family.

Secretaries and receptionists may be responsible for ensuring the appropriate certification forms are available when required (Figure 4.3).

IN CONFIDENCE   **CERTIFICATE A**

ABORTION ACT 1967

Not to be destroyed within three years of the date of operation

**Certificate to be completed before an abortion is
performed under Section 1(1) of the Act**

I, ...
(Name and qualifications of practitioner in block capitals)

of ....

....
(Full address of practitioner)

Have/have not* seen/and examined* the pregnant woman to whom this certificate relates at

....

....
(full address of place at which patient was seen or examined)

on ....

and I ....
(Name and qualifications of practitioner in block capitals)

of ....

....
(Full address of practitioner)

Have/have not* seen/and examined* the pregnant woman to whom this certificate relates at

....

....
(Full address of place at which patient was seen or examined)

on ....

We hereby certify that we are of the opinion, formed in good faith, that in the case

of ....
(Full name of pregnant woman in block capitals)

of ....

....
(Usual place of residence of pregnant woman in block capitals)

(Ring appro-priate letter(s))		
	A	the continuance of the pregnancy would involve risk to the life of the pregnant woman greater than if the pregnancy were terminated;
	B	the termination is necessary to prevent grave permanent injury to the physical or mental health of the pregnant woman;
	C	the pregnancy has NOT exceeded its 24th week and that the continuance of the pregnancy would involve risk, greater than if the pregnancy were terminated, of injury to the physical or mental health of the pregnant woman;
	D	the pregnancy has NOT exceeded its 24th week and that the continuance of the pregnancy would involve risk, greater than if the pregnancy were terminated, of injury to the physical or mental health of any existing child(ren) of the family of the pregnant woman;
	E	there is a substantial risk that if the child were born it would suffer from such physical or mental abnormalities as to be seriously handicapped.

This certificate of opinion is given before the commencement of the treatment for the termination of pregnancy to which it refers and relates to the circumstances of the pregnant woman's individual case.

Signed ....   **Date** ....

Signed ....   **Date** ....

* Delete as appropriate   Printed in the U.K. for H.M.S.O. 5/91 Dd. DH001306 C10000 38806 C3994   Form HSA1 (revised 1991)

Figure 4.3   Abortion certification form (sample).

Health and safety at work

The legislation relating to health and safety at work is complex, and although not directly responsible for workplace standards, medical secretaries and receptionists should be aware of the implications of the Health and Safety at Work etc. Act 1974 and of their personal responsibilities.

Health and Safety at Work etc. Act 1974

This Act, passed in 1974, is of direct importance to individuals, whether as managers responsible for the safety of staff immediately under their control, or as a member of the team responsible for the health and safety standards in the surgery, hospital outpatient department or clinic. The Health and Safety at Work etc. Act 1974 is a criminal statute and the Health and Safety Executive (HSE) is the enforcement body. Failure to carry out any duty under the Act is an offence and can lead to prosecution.

The aim of the legislation is to provide and create workplace standards for the reduction of known hazards, provision of a safe working environment for employees and adequate training and supervision given as is necessary to ensure, so far as is reasonably practicable, the health and safety at work of employees. All employers must fulfil this obligation. The term 'reasonably practicable' may be inferred from case law and the advice of HSE inspectors.

HSE inspectors have considerable powers, and may enter premises to enforce the law. Although they do not need to ask permission before doing so, they usually telephone to arrange a visit. Sanctions may be imposed upon those who have unlawfully created or permitted hazards, even where nobody has suffered an accident or ill health.

Employees themselves are obliged to take reasonable care to help in meeting this statutory requirement ('legal duty of care').

Duties of employers and employees

The duties arising from the Health and Safety at Work etc. Act 1974 are not difficult to apply. The legislation requires an employer (including a self-employed person, e.g. a GP) to provide and maintain a safe working environment and it establishes powers and penalties to enforce this. The main aim of the Act is to make both employers and employees conscious of the need for safety in all aspects of their work.

Employers' general duties to staff

The most important duty which every employer should fulfil is 'to ensure as far as is reasonably practicable, the health, safety and welfare at work of all his employees' (Health and Safety at Work etc. Act 1974).

Written statement of safety policy

An employer should provide information, training and supervision for staff on health and safety matters. Unless there are fewer than five staff, employers must provide a statement of general policy on health and safety and ensure it is implemented; employees should be consulted on its form and content. The written statement may be included in your employment contract. However, in a medical practice, with fewer than five staff, it is not necessary to give everyone a copy, and the statement can be displayed in a public place.

Safety representatives

Safety representatives are usually appointed if an employer recognizes a trade union, e.g. hospitals, health centres. They have a right to challenge the employer on all health and safety matters.

Duties to others using the hospital or surgery

An employer must ensure the safety of anyone using the premises, including patients, medical and pharmaceutical representatives, visitors, builders, tradesmen and health authority staff.

The Act requires the hospital, surgery or clinic to be run so as to ensure that all users of the premises are safe from risks of personal injury, and consideration should be given as to whether there are any potential hazards to elderly or disabled patients.

Notifying accidents and dangerous occurrences

An employer should keep a record of accidents. The HSE should be informed of certain serious accidents occurring to anyone using the premises.

Employees' responsibilities

Staff are required to take reasonable care of their own health and safety on the premises, and of the safety of other users of the premises who may be affected by their actions or omissions, and are expected to co-operate with the employer in carrying out these duties. Although employees' duties technically apply while at work, it would be wise to assume that these also apply throughout the time they are on the premises, for example when preparing coffee or lunch in a staff rest room.

Staff must not interfere with or misuse any health and safety equipment; for example, fire exits, fire extinguishers and warning notices.

Health and safety at work – regulations

In January 1993, six new sets of health and safety at work regulations came into force. They apply to almost all kinds of work activity in hospitals and general practice. Like the health and safety law, they place duties on employers to protect:

- their employees

- others, including members of the public who may be affected by the work being done.

These new regulations are needed to implement six European Community (EC) directives on health and safety at work. At the same time, they are part of the continuing modernization of UK law, and cover:

- health and safety management

- work equipment safety

- manual handling of loads

- workplace conditions

- personal protective equipment

- display screen equipment.

The new regulations require employers to:

- assess the risk to the health and safety of their employees and anyone else who may be affected by their work in order to identify any necessary preventative and protective measures. Employers with five or more employees should write their risk assessment down

- make arrangements for putting into practice the preventative and protective measures that follow from this risk assessment: they should cover planning, organization control and monitoring and review (i.e. the management of health and safety). Again, any employer with five or more employees must put these arrangements in writing

- carry out health surveillance of employees when appropriate

- appoint a competent person (normally an employee) to help devise and apply the protective steps that the risk assessment shows to be necessary

- set up emergency procedures

- give employees information on health and safety matters

- co-operate on health and safety matters with other employers sharing the same premises (e.g. other health authorities)
- make sure employees have adequate health and safety training and are capable enough at their job to avoid risk
- give whatever health and safety information temporary staff need to meet their specific needs.

These regulations also:

- place duties on all employees to follow health and safety instructions and report danger
- extend current health and safety laws which require employers to consult employees' safety representatives and provide facilities for them.

Provision and use of work equipment

These regulations pull together and tidy up various laws governing equipment used at work. These regulations:

- place general duties on all employers
- list minimum requirements for work equipment to deal with selected hazards which apply across all industries and sectors.

Generally speaking, these regulations make explicit what is already provided for elsewhere in current legislation or in good practice. Organizations that have well-chosen and well-maintained equipment need not do any more. The general duties of these regulations require organizations to:

- take into account the working conditions and hazards in the workplace when choosing equipment
- make sure equipment is suitable for the use intended and that it is properly maintained
- give adequate information, instruction and training.

Manual handling

These regulations replace patchy, old-fashioned and largely ineffective legislation, with a modern ergonomic approach to the problems of manual handling. They are important because the incorrect handling of loads may cause injuries, resulting in pain, time off work and even permanent disablement.

They apply to any manual handling operations which may cause injury at work. The manual handling assessment is a specific requirement under this regulation. The safety management regulations specifically ask employers to carry out risk assessment on hazards other than those already required under other regulations, for example, manual handling, COSHH, noise at work regulations, etc. They include not only lifting loads, but also lowering, pushing, pulling, carrying or moving them, whether by hand or other bodily force. Again, these regulations are supported by general guidance.

There are health care areas where staff are at risk in this respect, for example, nursing. Employers have to take four key steps.

1　Avoid hazardous manual handling operations when reasonably practicable.
2　Assess adequately any hazardous operations that cannot be avoided.
3　Reduce the risk of injury as far as possible.
4　Review assessments when changes take place.

Workplace health, safety and welfare

These regulations tidy up a lot of existing legislation, replacing some 35 pieces of old law. They are much easier to understand and make it far clearer what is expected. They cover many aspects of health, safety and welfare in the workplace, setting general requirements in four broad areas:

1　*Working environment* – temperature, ventilation, lighting, room dimensions, suitability of work stations.
2　*Safety* – safe passage of pedestrians and vehicles, windows and sky-lights (safe opening, closing and cleaning), safe materials and marking for transparent doors and partitions, doors, gates and escalators (safety devices), safe doors, gates and escalators, floors, falls from heights and falling objects.
3　*Facilities* – toilets, washing, eating and changing facilities, clothing storage, seating, rest areas, arrangements for non-smokers, rest facilities for pregnant women and nursing mothers.
4　*Housekeeping* – maintenance of workplace, equipment and facilities, cleanliness, and removal of waste materials.

Employers should ensure premises comply with the regulations.

Personal protective equipment

These regulations set out sound principles for selecting, providing, maintaining and using personal protective equipment (PPE). They are not directly relevant to medical secretaries and receptionists so further information would appear inappropriate.

Display screen equipment (DSE)

Unlike most of the regulations previously listed, the health and safety (display screen equipment) regulations do not replace old legislation, but cover a new area of work activity. Working with DSE is not generally risky, but it can lead to musculoskeletal problems, eye fatigue and mental stress. Problems of this kind can be overcome by good ergonomic design of equipment, furniture, the working environment and the tasks performed.

The regulations apply to DSE where there is a 'user', i.e. an employee who habitually uses it as a significant part of normal work. They cover equipment used for the display of text, numbers and graphics, regardless of the display process used.

These regulations include:

- assessing DSE workstations and reducing risks which are identified

- making sure workstations satisfy minimum requirements set for the DSE itself – keyboard, desk and chair, working environment and task design and software

- planning DSE work, so that there are breaks or changes in activity

- providing information and training for DSE users.

DSE users are entitled to appropriate eye and eyesight tests, and to special glasses if they are needed and normal ones cannot be used. Again these regulations are supported by detailed guidelines which are contained in the Health and Safety Executive's Guidance Note on DSE Work.

The Control of Substances Hazardous to Health Regulations (COSHH) 1994

COSHH regulations set out guidelines for the control of hazardous substances to employers, who have an obligation to protect people exposed to such substances.

The regulations include virtually all substances which are hazardous to health, and clearly set out the essential measures which employers, self-employed, and sometimes employees, have to take. Failure to comply constitutes an offence under the Health and Safety at Work etc. Act 1974. Substances hazardous to health include those labelled as:

- dangerous

- toxic

- harmful

- irritant

- corrosive.

The regulations give guidelines to employers which are based upon principles of occupational hygiene, the key duties being:

- to identify substances hazardous to health in the workplace

- to formally assess (in writing) the risk to employees from these materials

- to control adequately and monitor the risk

- to provide health surveillance where appropriate

- to provide adequate instruction and training.

Other less dangerous substances covered by the regulations include disinfectants, clinical wastes and cleaning materials.

GPs, health authorities and other health care employers should consider how COSHH applies to the working environment and to their employees, for example:

- the risk from biocides and sterilizing agents

- the risk of staff contracting infection from biological samples and waste

- policies and specific procedures are necessary for cleaning medical equipment, and safe disposal of drugs, contaminated needles, dressings and appliances

- staff vaccination status should be reviewed.

Summary of legal aspects

This section has attempted to give an overview of the many and diverse legal aspects involving the work of medical secretaries and receptionists.

On a more personal note, information has been given to provide a basic knowledge and understanding of legislation influencing the duties and rights of employees and employers working in organizations, large or small.

5

Health and safety in a clinical environment

Introduction

General principles of health and safety at work have already been discussed in some detail. On a practical issue, how does it affect the secretary and receptionist working in a clinical environment?

The Health and Safety at Work etc. Act requires:

- *That any 'plant' in the workplace is safe* – The term plant covers equipment in the work environment, including heaters, sterilizers, electric kettles, plugs and examination couches.

  Potential hazards include someone getting a shock from an electric kettle due to a plug incorrectly fitted or a patient being injured because an examination couch collapses. Occurrences such as these could lead to a charge of having unsafe plant on the premises and ensuing liability. Electrical and mechanical equipment needs servicing at least annually.

- *That systems of work are safe* – It is important that day-to-day work systems are safe and do not lead to injury. Safe systems normally refer to policy and procedures, e.g. manual handling risk assessment and the use of gloves while handling specimens.

- *That premises are safe* – This includes floors which are uneven and/or slippery or dangerous when wet, outside steps which are uneven and/or unlit at night, and ceilings in danger of collapse, which could all be considered as unsafe.

First aid at work

Regulations require employers to make adequate provision for their employees in case of injury or if they should become unwell at work. It is advisable, but not mandatory, to have a qualified first aider, although a doctor or a nurse could become an 'appointed person' – but there must be an appointed person available at all times. This person is to take charge of the situation should a serious injury or illness occur in the workplace and is responsible for the first aid equipment. An 'appointed person' if not fully trained should have attended a short course in first aid lasting a minimum of four hours, which should include:

- resuscitation
- control of bleeding
- treatment of the unconscious casualty.

Hazardous substances in the workplace

Control of Substances Hazardous to Health (COSHH) regulations have already been mentioned. Receptionists and secretaries should be aware of hazards arising from the handling, transport, storage and disposal of hazardous substances. Control measures must be in place to ensure that their place of work is not in breach of the law.

Clinical waste

Clinical waste is waste arising from medical practice that may provide a hazard or give offence unless rendered safe and inoffensive. Such waste includes human or animal tissue, or excretion, drugs and medicinal products, swabs, dressings, instruments or similar substances and materials.

All staff involved in areas where clinical waste arises should be given instruction in waste handling, segregation, storage and disposal procedures, and where appropriate, the use of protective clothing.

Waste segregation

This is achieved by readily identifiable colour-coded containers or plastic bags:

- *Black* – Normal household waste only
- *Yellow* – Clinical waste for incineration.

There are different categories of waste and different procedures for each category. These include:

- soiled surgical dressings, swabs and other contaminated waste from consulting rooms and treatment areas
- syringes, needles, cartridges and glass ampoules ('sharps'). It is dangerous to dispose of 'sharps' in yellow bags as this is a potential cause of needle-stick injuries
- laboratory waste in medical practice, including blood samples, vomit or sputum
- solid dose medicinal products, small volume injectables, vaccine and sera*
- urine samples.

Secretaries and receptionists will be given appropriate instructions for disposal if necessary. However, the following guidelines should be understood by all those working in medical practice.

Storage of clinical waste

Waste bags must be kept secure from unauthorized persons and entry by animals whilst awaiting collection. They must never be left outside where children may play, or drug addicts may find used syringes and needles.

Removal of clinical waste

This is arranged on a local basis. Health authorities/health boards will advise on the availability of a collection service. Organizations providing this will arrange to supply services and arrange collection and incineration.

---

* *Note:* All controlled drugs covered by the Misuse of Drugs Act require special procedures before they can be destroyed. Unused drugs are usually returned to the pharmacy for safe disposal.

Specimens

Handling specimens

Receptionists in general practice may find that patients leave various specimens on the reception counter unwrapped. It is the receptionist's duty to protect herself and colleagues from potential infection by handling these specimens correctly, for example either ask the patient to place the specimen in a plastic bag, or use a pair of disposable gloves to handle the specimen. The same system could be used for handling used medicine containers, dressings, tissues, hearing aids, etc.

Transport of specimens

Specimens to be sent to the pathology laboratory by the local collection service must be clearly labelled and accompanied by pathology request forms. Specimens to be sent by post must be packaged in a rigid container with absorbent packing and sent by first-class letter post. The address of the sender should be clearly written on the outside of the package so that the post office can contact the sender if the package is damaged to find out the risk to the handler. Specimens sent through the post must be clearly labelled 'Pathological Specimen – Handle with Care'.

Hepatitis and AIDS

Receptionists are at risk where blood, semen and other body fluids of an infected person can enter the body, for example, through an open cut. All scratches, cuts and grazes must be covered with a waterproof covering.

When body fluid has to be mopped up, disposable plastic or latex gloves, a disposable plastic apron and paper tissues must be used *whether or not* infection is present. After use, these items must be placed in a clinical waste collection unit for incineration. Clothing may be cleaned by washing on a hot-cycle. Hard surfaces and floors can be wiped/washed with a freshly prepared 10% bleach solution. Skin that has been in contact should be washed with soap and water. Mouth-to-mouth resuscitation should be carried out with a mouthpiece if available. Common sense measures and good hygiene are the best measures to prevent infection.

The chances of staff being infected with hepatitis is considerably higher than with AIDS as the virus survives room temperature for a much longer duration. Hepatitis B vaccination is available to staff for protection.

Fire Precautions Act 1971

This is the Act covering fire regulations. However, in medical practices with less than 20 people working, there is no need for a fire certificate. Larger organizations, e.g. hospitals and health centres, will have regular fire drills. The local fire officer will check the provision of fire alarms, extinguishers and hoses, that fire exits are not obstructed and signs are readily visible. Provision of emergency light supplies are checked.

Medical practices should have their own plans and clearly defined procedures to be followed in the event of fire. Basic guidelines would include:

- prevention – check for hazards and try to prevent a fire from happening

- fire alert/warning – who will raise the alarm and dial 999? Who will evacuate the surgery? What is the system for ensuring that everyone in the building knows about it? How to stop more patients from entering

- evacuation – procedures for evacuating the building. Marshall all staff and patients to one assembly point. How do you ensure no one is missing?

- security – people are most important. Leave behind all valuables, except the appointment book which will tell you if anyone is missing. This should be taken to the assembly point

- informing staff and public – a notice should be displayed telling people what to do in the event of fire. The notice indicates the assembly point and the action to be taken in the event of a fire.

Clinical risk management

Although risk management is not new, its application to clinical medicine is a relatively new concept in the UK. It is a response to increasing medical litigation but, in addition to reducing the chance (or cost) of litigation, it should lead to improved patient care. In a hospital one of the greatest areas of risk in financial terms arises from patient treatment. Clinical risk management programmes require the active involvement of senior and junior medical staff, nurses and other health care professionals. Clinical risk management may be categorized in the following areas:

- accident prevention
- damage limitation.

Accident prevention means taking steps to avoid adverse outcomes and includes the following:

- continuing medical education

- clinical audit

- protocols and guidelines for treatment

- the application of results from previous claims.

For example, a primary prevention step may be for a new member of staff in accident and emergency to know which facilities are immediately available and how and when to summon more experienced assistance.

Damage limitation measures either help in the investigation of a problem, or are steps taken to ensure events or incidents are routinely investigated.

Clinical risk management is not about gathering information and form filling but rather concerned with identifying and analysing the risk and then controlling the risk. Controlling the risk is the most important element, as the ultimate aim is accident prevention.

Coping with aggression and violence

Dealing with aggressive callers

Receptionists and secretaries working in the field of health care face a number of patients and callers who are potentially violent, for example, the mentally disturbed, the emotionally upset, or those who are suffering from the effects of drugs or drink.

Your organization will, no doubt, have a policy for dealing with potentially violent patients. If so, it is up to you to ensure you know what it is and what you should do. Remember, most of the patients attending your hospital or your surgery are seeking understanding, help and advice about their problems which are causing them a certain amount of anxiety. They may become frustrated and aggrieved as they wait for their appointments.

As the patient becomes more upset, it can lead to aggression and the receptionist or secretary may be the focus of this aggression. Always deal as quickly as possible with any patient who becomes agitated, especially if they seem to be under the influence of drugs or drink. Make sure you alert the doctor or nurse to the problem as soon as possible.

When a confrontation is building up, try to defuse the situation by talking to the patient in a calm manner, and attempt to reduce that patient's agitation. You may be able to distract the patient from his/her particular grievance and cool the situation.

You should be on guard to protect yourself from physical attack. In trying to appear relaxed and natural you may, for example, put your hands in your pockets; this will leave you defenceless to a blow. If possible, always get a physical barrier between you and the aggressor, such as a counter or a desk. Discreetly try to attract the attention of another member of staff if it seems as if the situation is going to erupt. If you have a buzzer 'alert' system, have a pre-arranged signal and use it.

Note: The best way to defend yourself from attack is to get out of the way as quickly as possible.

Coping with a personal attack

A personal attack is unlikely to happen, and if you take common sense precautions you can reduce the risk. Unfortunately, some attacks do occur and you should give some thought about what you should do if you become a victim.

Always remember that personal safety should come before property. Is it worth being injured for the sake of a prescription or some tablets? The police would prefer you uninjured and in a position to give them an accurate description of the attacker.

It is worth considering what you would be prepared to do in self defence should you be attacked. If other people are near, then you must shout to attract their attention. Only you can decide whether to fight back. A woman has the right to defensive action using reasonable force in the case of an attack, for example, by kicking, scratching or by the use of items which are accepted as normally being carried:

- hair spray

- bunch of keys

- umbrella

- personal attack alarm.

It must be pointed out, however, that legally you may not carry offensive weapons.

If you are sexually assaulted or raped, it is important that you contact the police immediately – for your own sake and for the safety of others. Always bear in mind:

- however difficult or unpleasant the thought, resist the need to wash or change your clothing – you could be removing important evidence

- do not drink alcohol or take any drugs that might prevent you from giving a clear account of what has happened

- try to remember as much as possible about your attacker.

The police will deal with you with care, understanding and complete confidentiality.

General security and safety in the surgery or hospital

- Challenge all suspicious persons.
- Do not be taken in by so-called workmen or officials; if they are genuine, they will not mind having their identity checked.
- Keep all valuables and prescription pads out of sight.
- Ensure petty cash is secured in a locked tin, and kept inside a locked drawer.
- Ensure consulting and treatment rooms are locked when not in use.
- If you have an identity badge, always wear it.
- Equipment should be security marked.
- Always keep your valuables with you, or lock them away.

Travelling to and from work or whenever you are out and about

You should always be alert to potential danger when travelling by car, public transport or on foot. Remember the following points.

- Think ahead. Get into a safe routine and always use it.
- Avoid walking home late at night.
- Walk purposefully. Do *not* accept lifts.
- When travelling by car, do not give lifts to strangers.
- On public transport sit near the guard, driver or other women passengers.
- Only use a reputable taxi cab firm. Ask the cab company for the driver's name and call sign.
- In the event of your car breaking down and waiting for help, keep doors and windows locked and sit in the passenger seat so it appears you are not alone.

- Avoid multi-storey car parks where possible.

- Carry a torch with you if travelling after dark.

Safety at the end of a surgery or clinic session

Always check that the premises are secure before you leave, and look outside to make sure that no one is lurking. If you see someone prowling or hanging around, stay inside and let someone know. If necessary, contact the police. If you are usually collected by car, wait until it arrives before going out. If you are travelling by public transport and are alone, do not leave so early that you have to wait a long time for the bus or train.

Finally, your local crime prevention officer attached to your nearest police station will be willing to talk to you and your colleagues about coping with aggression and violence and give practical help and advice to women on their personal safety.

6

Practical reception skills in general practice

Introduction

Every receptionist is gifted in some way, for example in dealing kindly with people, having patience, a pleasant speaking voice, etc. In addition to these natural gifts everyone can acquire skills to help them to do their job better. The most important skill areas are those of communication and organization which are covered in other areas of this text. However, there are some skills which are unique to a receptionist in general practice.

All approaches to the receptionist are by patients, or their relatives, who believe that they have a need. They cannot see 'behind the scenes' in the surgery or have any real understanding of the pressures on doctors and receptionists. Receptionists must always bear in mind the perceived need of the patient, no matter how insignificant from the surgery perspective. Patients are concerned about either their own state of health or that of a family member. It is very important, therefore, that the skills to recognize how patients are feeling and deal sensitively with them are used constantly. The issues of non-verbal communication and related issues are covered in Chapter 2.

The person responsible for controlling the flow of patients into a number of doctors consulting at the same time needs to have a good system, to concentrate and remain alert. If other members are fully co-operative in matters like ensuring the appointments book, or surgery lists, are clearly written, or appropriately 'marking off' a patient as arriving, or having been sent into the doctor, then the task is made simpler. However, the person controlling the surgery flow tends to be the one to whom everyone turns with queries – Where are Mrs A's results? Where are the notes for child B? Do I need to do a claim form for child health surveillance? How many extras are there? When will Dr C be free to see the rep? and so on. If telephone answering also is part of the picture, it can be very diffi-cult to keep on top of who is where, and what needs to be dealt with next.

Smooth surgery flow is made easier if the preparation for surgeries has been carried out properly. Where an appointment system is used it is sen-sible to take out all the medical records well before the start of surgery and check that all test results and hospital letters relating to these records have been filed. It can also help the practice finances if stickers are used on the records to indicate that smears are due or pill forms need to be signed, which the receptionist can then act upon by drawing the doctor's attention with a note, or completing a claim ready for signature.

As patients leave the consulting room, follow-up appointments need to be arranged and appropriate advice given about requirements for some health promotion clinics, e.g. to bring a urine sample. Maintaining neat work areas during consulting times makes tidying at the end of surgery considerably easier. However, even if it is not possible to keep tidy at the busiest times it is important that quieter times are used to the fullest to return working areas to order, file medical records, check that doctors' rooms have been tidied and stocks of disposables topped up.

Telephone answering can be an especially difficult task for the doctor's receptionist. Any incoming call may be about a patient who is bleeding, appearing to have a heart attack, or some other medical crisis with a child. Therefore, the procedure for dealing with emergencies must be clear and the telephone must never be left to ring for an indefinite period. The tele-phone must be answered in preference to dealing with a patient standing at the reception desk – however, it is also essential that any patient at the desk is acknowledged with a smile, so that they know they will be dealt with when you are free.

The receptionist is also required to be a fount of all knowledge, for example, the following can be helpful in finding and giving out appropri-ate information efficiently:

- keeping telephone directories of often-used numbers, or hospital inter-nal directories, along with other service information sources

- list of subjects of leaflets kept available for patients in the waiting room and brief notes on developments in trends in health promotion

- awareness of changes to surgeries and clinics, changes in local hospi-tal, community and social services.

It is especially important that the receptionist knows the limits of her own authority, i.e. when and to whom to refer for advice.

The receptionist is also responsible for keeping an eye on the waiting area to:

- make sure that the patients who are obviously unwell are not troubled by unduly active children

- maintain a pleasant ambience, by ensuring adequate ventilation or heat

- tidy the waiting area of toys, magazines and leaflets at the end of each surgery or clinic.

Thankfully, it will rarely be necessary to clean up whilst patients are waiting, for example, if a patient is literally sick in the waiting area or walks something unpleasant-smelling from the pavement into the surgery!

Keeping the doctors happy is yet another set of tasks for the receptionist. Most of the time this will entail keeping the surgery flow steady, not allowing too many interruptions in consultations, providing tea or coffee at the right times, and making sure that records, results, letters and other essentials are all available when required. Not too much to ask!

Individually controlling surgery flow, answering the telephone, dealing with patients at the desk, and keeping the doctor happy are not too difficult to achieve as separate items, but in the real world of the reception office, there is rarely the opportunity to concentrate on one task at a time. The skill is in being able to constantly readjust priorities, without forgetting the ones that slip to the bottom of the mental pile.

Dividing up the duties so that, for instance, one person controls surgery flow, another majors on answering the telephone, another does repeat scripts and perhaps deals with queries, can go some way to lessening the pressure. However, it is also impossible to remain rigidly with such a plan. It is essential that receptionists work in a team, not only being aware of keeping on top of what they are supposed to be doing, but having their eyes open to see when a colleague needs help, and being able to adjust their own priorities to step into the breach.

Various tools, like log books, message books, having good systems in place, clear procedures for dealing with routine issues, knowing whom to turn to with queries, all help. However, the ability to juggle ten priorities at one time is both an art and a gift. Being self-controlled, planning work, and being as efficient about it as possible means that anyone with a degree of intelligence, who wants to, can achieve a certain degree of competency. However, there will always be some people who enjoy this kind of pressure (only feeling the strain sometimes) and those to whom it is a strain all the time.

First impressions

First impressions count. A receptionist will often be the patient's initial point of contact with the organization, and they will make assumptions, positive or negative, about the treatment they are likely to receive from that first point.

Record keeping and general administration

In any business it is essential to keep records. For example, where a receptionist may be delegated the task of keeping control of stocks of forms and stationery, or petty cash, it is essential that adequate documentation is maintained. Alternatively a receptionist is likely to pass messages to a variety of people in the course of a working day. Keeping a record of messages ensures that not only does the right message get passed, but who took the message, who received it and when, can all be substantiated.

Written communication

Although technology is coming on apace there is still the need for hand-written communication – messages and notes to one another. It is obvious that any hand-written communication should be legible, but often in haste it is easy to forget that, and to fail to ensure that any other person should be able to read a scrawled message, entry in an appointment book or list of names, etc.

Messages

Some offices have pre-printed message forms which prompt message takers to collect all the necessary information as they go. Another option is to use a message book with columns drawn up, so that it is easy to check if a message has been received. It is important not only that there should be adequate systems for communicating messages, but responsibility is taken to ensure that the systems work properly.

Message boards

Dry-wipe white boards are extremely useful for putting up short-term reminders and messages, provided one person is delegated responsibility for clearing off messages as soon as they become redundant!

Letters and memos

Receptionists may be required to send out letters and memos. As a general rule this is likely to be routine (standard) documents, where a master copy is used to generate photocopies, into which names and addresses, dates, data, can be inserted by hand. However, technology has made it possible for receptionists with little or no formal training in secretarial or word-processing skills to generate printed letters from the computer. It is important to remember that the image of the practice/hospital is presented via written communication and therefore it is important that presentation standards are met. There are conventions about letter layout, e.g. whether commas are used at the end of every line in an address or how many spaces are left between the end of a letter and 'Yours sincerely'. Where training is not given in these details a poor impression will be given to anyone who expects normal conventions to be observed. Therefore, the setting of practice standards is a valuable guide to ensure that everyone produces written communication to the same standard.

Organization

Systems and organization are essential to the smooth running of a reception area. Some are blessed with a natural ability to be organized. Those who are not need to apply far more self-discipline to initiate and maintain systems. Everyone needs to know what is expected of whom, using what, and by when.

Similarly, individuals need to be organized in their use of time. The receptionist who retains control of the tasks to be completed avoids personal stress. Too much stress will inevitably lead to mistakes, poor handling of patients, and a general deterioration in standards of service.

Take time out to:

- make a list of the tasks you perform every day, every week, once a month

    - make a week plan

    - block off the times on the week plan you have no option but to be 'demand driven', e.g. on reception desk for a busy surgery/clinic

    - fit other tasks around these blocks at the optimum time

- make a 'to do' list

    - break down big items into small stages

    - realistically allocate items from your 'to do' list into your working week

- discuss your findings with your supervisor so that any queries regarding priorities can be settled to their satisfaction.

Using the simple example of stocks of forms, unless there is a system for ensuring that stocks are maintained there is every likelihood that either one day stores will run out or that scarce storage space is taken up by unnecessarily large supplies.

Since there are many supplies needed it is helpful if a system is set up and maintained with the same degree of commitment from everyone.

Initial skill is needed to think through the best and simplest way of organizing any particular aspect of reception. After that, discipline and commitment from all team members are essential to maintain the system.

Maintaining the office and reception areas

In order to ensure the comfort and well-being of patients, relatives and other visitors, effort needs to be made to keep public areas tidy and smart. This must be a priority, because untidiness can be a hazard and gives a general impression of sloppiness.

Ensure that:

- the area is kept tidy and free from hazards. Some visitors are likely to have visual or physical disabilities

- hazards are reported promptly and immediate action taken to minimize the danger

- fire exits are clearly indicated and kept unobstructed

- notices and information leaflets are kept up to date, and are clearly and neatly displayed

- an up-to-date supply of magazines, etc. is available for visitors to read.

Mail

Mail should be correctly sorted and date stamped on receipt. Any enclosures should be securely attached and missing items reported promptly. The mail should then be passed to the appropriate person for action.

When sending mail out check that names and addresses are correct and clearly legible. Envelopes and parcels should be securely sealed. All the mail you deal with should be handled promptly as it relates to patients' health and any delay could be dangerous.

If you are suspicious of any mail received, local security arrangements should be followed. Check with your manager if you are unfamiliar with these.

Stock control

The purpose of stock control system is to keep track of such items as stationery, computer hardware, drugs, dressings, linen, sundry equipment, etc. that the practice possesses. A stock control system is necessary to avoid two pitfalls:

1   *Having too much stock.* Money tied up in stock cannot be used for any other purpose, and if the stock is perishable or becomes obsolete as time passes, it may be difficult to recover this money in full.
2   *Having too little stock.* If essential items are short, patients may face long delays or inconvenience.

The ideal situation, and the one that a good stock control system aims to produce, is to have adequate stock on hand – neither too much nor too little.

Stock control also acts as a deterrent to wastage and pilfering. A good system will show up when losses are occurring, and the knowledge of this may deter pilferers. It should also highlight the points at which losses are likely to occur from other causes.

Records of stock levels are obviously essential to any large-scale control system; a hospital which does not keep control of stocks is likely to find it very hard to control them efficiently. The records may be on index cards, or a computerized stock control system may be in operation. Goods are stored until they are needed, and are released by the storekeeper only when he or she is presented with a duly authorized document, such as a requisition note.

Petty cash

Small amounts of expenditure for goods or services are usually paid for out of petty cash since the amounts are too small to be paid by cheque; for example, stamps, milk bills, small stationery items. Secretarial or clerical staff may be responsible for controlling petty cash and the system most commonly used is known as the *imprest* system.

The imprest amount is drawn from the account each week or month, through the main cash book. The sum is estimated to cover all small expenses throughout the agreed period, and is referred to as the 'imprest' or 'float'. The petty cash is kept in a locked cash box. During the month, payments are made from the imprest, and all expenditure must be covered by a petty cash voucher or a receipt. The voucher should be signed by the person receiving the money. The vouchers and receipts should be numbered and filed for purposes of audit.

A separate petty cash book is maintained analysing the expenditure, and at the end of the month a sum of money is drawn by cheque to restore the amount of the imprest to the original sum.

Helping to maintain a safe environment

Health and safety at work legislation is intended to safeguard all employees, patients and visitors to the workplace. Individual employees are required to ensure that they do not endanger their own health or safety, or that of their colleagues, patients or visitors. Potentially dangerous situations and unknown or potentially hazardous substances must be treated with the utmost care.

The legislation is detailed and complex. As a minimum, all staff must ensure that:

- there are no trailing wires

- filing cabinet drawers are kept closed

- chairs and other obstacles do not block walkways or fire escapes

- fire extinguishers and exits are clearly indicated

- any known hazards are marked clearly and problems reported to the appropriate manager

- visitors are informed of any known hazards

- potentially violent situations are defused as far as is possible

- care is taken when handling specimens, especially over spillages, and hands are washed after undertaking this task.

Coping with aggression and violence

Communication is often the key when dealing with conflict of this kind. Good communication can play a vital part in defusing potentially difficult situations or avoiding them altogether, but equally, poor communication can increase levels of frustration and anger which then erupt in violence (see Chapter 5). We have to consider carefully what messages our words and movements are conveying. Are they contradictory? We can tell when someone is saying one thing but means something quite different. Perhaps it is someone we know well, and can therefore judge their statements on the basis of what we know of them, but it is equally likely that they are strangers, and the truth is conveyed by their stance, facial movements, etc. (see Chapter 2).

Procedures manuals

Many organizations are using Standard Operating Procedures (SOPs) as part of implementing BS5750. These SOPs state who does what, how they should do it, how often, etc.

Within reception offices there may not be the need to have SOPs for every activity or task, but a manual of key procedures may be helpful. The administrative processes of stock control and petty cash are two examples which should be documented in a specific procedure. The procedure document may be as little as one side of A4 with the vital information summarized into a table, but it should include who is responsible, what steps are taken, how frequently, and any special notes. Filing these procedure sheets into a loose-leaf folder allows additional procedures to be added or existing procedures to be updated whenever necessary. Apart from encouraging a uniform approach to carrying out tasks, these written procedures form a useful resource especially for new staff who may have been told how to do something, but have forgotten or need to clarify details.

Information technology (IT)

Practices still vary enormously in their modes of working, in size, number of staff, equipment available, and capability of using their technology.

Computer

Where a practice has the patient database on computer the advantages include:

- logging and generation of repeat prescriptions
- checking registration status
- checking immunization/smear status
- checking health promotion data.

If this is linked into an appointments system the difficulties of manual appointment books, e.g. illegible writing, pages messy with cancellations, two people not being able to use the book at the same time, hand-written surgery lists for pulling out records, are all circumvented.

The major disadvantage is when the system 'goes down', all this increased efficiency disappears and returning to manual methods, no matter how temporarily, results in unavoidable delays and disruption.

Reference has been made to IT for written communication in Chapter 10. Suffice to say here that staff who could only ever write letters are now able to use wordprocessing to generate mailmerged letters, or produce their own letters to patients with very little training. Spreadsheets can be used either to collect data (for display in tables, graphs and pie charts) or to present doctor and staff rotas.

Desktop publishing software can be used to generate leaflets, posters and handouts. Technology saves time for some tasks: in others it does not save time, but it does make it possible to produce professional-looking documents, e.g. rota charts, posters.

For those who enjoy using the computer it is essential that the computer does not become an obstacle between the patient and the receptionist. It is equally rude to continue to type away absorbed by the machine as it is to continue to talk to a colleague or take a telephone call without acknowledging the presence of a patient.

The advantage of technology to receptionists include:

* ease of presenting professional standard documents, speed of finding, generating and transmitting information

* efficiency in dealing with issues.

The major disadvantages to receptionists include:

* reliance upon the electronics so that in the event of the computer 'being down' everything has to go on hold

* the danger of losing the personal touch.

Fax

The fax machine has several important uses in general practice:

* to return urgent blood results
* notification of discharge from maternity wards
* to pass complex information
* make claims to health authority/health board re patient registration etc.

In general the advantages and disadvantages to the receptionist using the fax machine may be summarized:

ADVANTAGES	DISADVANTAGES
Cheaper than using the telephone (if it takes less time than to say it)	Breach of confidentiality if fax goes to the wrong address
Much quicker than the post	Fax paper may fade with time, so it is important either to photocopy or file the original

Modern fax machines which use plain paper do not have the problem of fading print.

The Internet

The Internet is a world-wide system of information technology networks, providing a global, on-line computer network connecting governments, universities, organizations and many other networks and users. The service provides:

*   access to information

*   on-line conversations

*   information exchange

*   conferences

*   electronic mail.

It also has the ability to access remote computers and send and retrieve files. It began in 1984 and is now estimated to have over 50 million users with an estimated one million new users joining each month.

Electronic mail

Electronic mail (e-mail) is a telecommunications system that enables the users of a computer network to send messages to other users throughout the world. Telephone wires are necessary to send the signals from terminal to terminal. E-mail subscribers may send messages by computer, by 'dropping' the communication into a central computer's memory bank by use of a modem. The recipient 'collects' the communication by means of an individual password and access-logging to safeguard against unauthorized user access into the system. Figure 6.1 shows the basic structure of an electronic mail system.

sending computer

receiving computer

central computer stores messages

A message is sent via a telephone line and stored in a central computer. The message remains there until the recipient calls up the central computer and collects the message.

Figure 6.1   The basic structure of an electronic mail system.

While many GPs still continue to request investigations on pathology request forms with results sent back to the practice on paper, e-mail is increasingly being used by some GPs to receive electronically the results of pathological tests initiated by the practice. The way in which electronic results are used will depend upon both the procedures and protocols within the practice and the features of the GP system linking with the hospital laboratory. The main benefits of laboratory links include:

- a significant reduction in the need for GPs or administrative staff to phone the laboratory for results

- releasing administrative staff time through not having to type in test results

- the patients are impressed!

Photocopying

The photocopier is a great time saver. However, lack of training in office standards and procedures can result in poor quality work and failure to maintain the equipment properly. Good quality originals are essential to producing fine quality copies. A ring binder can be kept near to the photocopier with photocopy originals in clear plastic wallets. (Yellow highlighter pen does not show up on the photocopies, so use one to write 'original' to ensure that the original is easily identifiable and does not get circulated.)

Costs can be kept down by reducing the number of poor quality copies by simple things such as:

* collecting a folder of good quality 'originals'

* ensuring that the original does not get used

* placing the original carefully, so that copies do not come out even slightly skew

* buying appropriate cleaners

* keeping the platen (the glass panel onto which copies are placed) clean

* never putting documents with wet correction fluid onto the platen

* delegating someone to be responsible for replacing the toner and keeping the copier clean.

The effect of technology on staff is to make their lives a lot easier in some ways, and to make aspects of work available to them for personal development; the disadvantage for people who are afraid of technology is that they may get left behind and their value falls because they cannot take an equal share in routine workloads.

A receptionist is now required to have a wide range of skills. Apart from dealing with people on the telephone and face to face, retrieving and filing medical records and filing away letters and reports, the receptionist generally needs to have keyboard skills and a willingness to learn how to use the latest technology.

Appointment systems in general practice

The role that the medical receptionist plays is crucial to the successful running of an appointment system. Nearly every patient who sees the doctor makes his or her first contact through the receptionist. The receptionist channels patients into the appointment system and runs the system once the surgery has started.

The receptionist has to calm the agitated patient, explain and cope with doctors' absences on emergencies, and acts to translate unstreamed demand into a rational framework.

It is important to run an appointment system as well as possible, both for the doctor and the patient's sake – even a few dissatisfied patients can lead very quickly to an unhappy practice. A well run system reflects the general efficiency of the practice, and puts less strain on GPs and their receptionists.

An efficient appointment system should benefit both doctor and patient:

Benefits to doctors

- effective organization of workload

- more efficient management of time

- limits the number of patients seen in one session

- patients records are left on their desks in advance of surgery session

- less waiting room space required

- the duration of consultation can be varied according to predetermined need

Benefits to patients

- able to plan their day

- should not have to wait a long time to see the doctor

- fewer people in the waiting room – less chance of cross-infection.

The perfect appointment system is neither too rigid to exclude emergencies, nor so chaotic that it keeps those who have made appointments waiting for an excessive length of time. The number of patients booked for each surgery session should bear a close relation to the speed at which the doctor works.

Patient dissatisfaction arises from not being able to get an appointment without delay. Appointment systems, therefore, should be flexible to allow for those patients with urgent problems to see their doctor very quickly.

The terms 'urgent' and 'emergency' are both subjective and emotive terms, and perhaps receptionists should be encouraged to delete them from their vocabulary! They could be replaced with 'will it wait until tomorrow?' However, your practice will have its own procedures for dealing with such requests from patients.

Types of appointment system

Times of booking for patients can be arranged in various ways and each practice or doctor will decide which system suits them best.

Whatever system is used, it is essential for the frequency of appointments to match the doctor's consultation rate, and for sufficient time to be left for patients who need to be seen and fitted in at short notice.

Your surgery may use one or a combination of the following types of booking:

- sequential booking

- block-release booking

- limited block booking.

All these systems have the flexibility for patients to be seen quickly if necessary. There are several ways to deal with 'extras' to be seen despite a full appointments book:

- they can be fitted in between booked appointments

- provision can be made for patients with urgent problems to be seen after the booked surgery

- one doctor in the practice, on a rotating basis, to act as 'mopper-up' and see the extras instead of carrying out a booked surgery

- block-release booking allows for 'holes' to be left in the appointments book which cannot be filled until the beginning of the day on which they are entered.

Whichever method your practice uses, it is essential that the receptionist knows exactly what to do.

Follow-up after missed appointments

Patients who fail to keep their appointments for cervical cytology and immunizations will either be sent a letter or telephoned with a further appointment. If patients do not attend, doctors may not achieve their targets for cervical cytology and child immunization.

The medical records of non-attendees for routine appointments may be marked 'DNA' or 'did not attend' and this information may also be entered on the practice computer. However, this procedure may vary according to practice protocol.

If the doctor has given the patient advice about follow-up appointments, tests, etc. it is important to check their understanding of the instructions given. They may need to be given a letter, or appointment card with the details of their next appointment. If a patient seems to be confused about what has been said, it is doubly important to encourage them to wait and have a word with the doctor or nurse before they leave. The patient may need to be directed to the correct place for any tests which are necessary. After the appointment, the notes will go to the secretary for any letters that are needed.

Many practices are now using a fully computerized appointments system to provide a more effective method of making appointments for their patients and to replace the appointments book which can only be used by one receptionist at a time. A major benefit to the practice is that appointments can be made by as many reception staff as there are terminals.

Medical records

A medical record is the history of a patient's treatment as an outpatient, inpatient or both. The record is vital because it provides a means of communication between doctors, nurses and other members of the care team about investigations, diagnosis, observations, treatment prescribed and progress. It acts as a reminder, and can be used as an educational instrument for trainees, for research, for informing medical negligence cases and other legal purposes, and for gathering statistics such as those that are needed for planning future services.

Records contain much confidential information, and all those with access to them have a legal responsibility to maintain confidentiality. Computerized records present a particular challenge to confidentiality. This is examined in more detail in Chapter 7.

Two recent Acts of Parliament allow individuals access to their medical information. The Access to Medical Reports Act 1988 gives an individual in England, Wales or Scotland the right to see medical reports prepared for insurance or employment purposes. The Access to Personal Files and Medical Reports Order 1991 for Northern Ireland affords similar rights there. The Access to Health Records Act 1990, which applies in England, Wales and Scotland, establishes an individual's right of access to their own medical records. In certain circumstances, access can be granted to other individuals. The Act also provides for the correction of inaccurate information. Access can be refused in certain cases if, in the opinion of the record holder, disclosure would cause serious harm to the patient. (See Chapter 4.)

Medical records were standardized when the NHS began to provide some uniformity between hospitals, although some local variation still exists.

In the United Kingdom, the medical records held by general practitioners are unique; they follow patients throughout their lives from the cradle to the grave. Medical records show patients' names, demographic details, and information of previous illnesses and significant episodes in the lives of their subjects, unlike hospital records which often only cover a specific episode of hospital attendance, e.g. appendicitis or hysterectomy.

The purpose of the medical record

The basic function of the medical record can best be described as an 'aide-memoire' (Figure 6.2):

- It gives a method of recording events in a person's life. It traces from birth the record of a patient's illnesses, treatments, investigations and other significant events.

- It is a channel of communication. The GP writes in the medical record, giving details of his/her findings, treatment and diagnosis of a

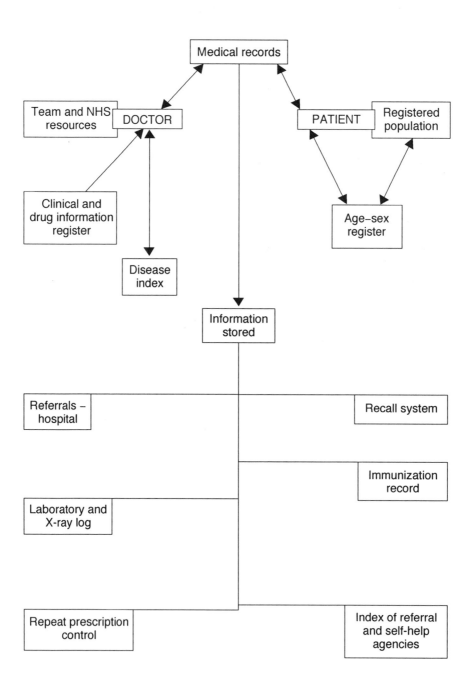

Figure 6.2   A model of the medical record information system.

patient's condition. This becomes a permanent record and communicates that information to those persons who have the right of access, for example, another partner in the practice, the practice nurse, or to another doctor at a later date.

- It acts as a record of outside health contacts. When the patient attends a hospital outpatient department, or has an investigation, information is provided, and if correctly filled in, the patient's record contributes to the total knowledge about the patient.

- It provides a record of all treatment and all the drugs given during a patient's lifetime.

- It is a medico-legal record. If a medical or legal problem arises at any time, the patient's medical records will be required to support any action taken.

THE FOUR MAIN FUNCTIONS OF MEDICAL RECORDS

A permanent record of significant events

A medico-legal record

A file for hospital and laboratory reports and letters

An aide-memoire

Thus, it is vital that medical records are kept securely and the information contained therein stored in an orderly, systematic way. This can be achieved by:

- ensuring that all the continuation sheets are in chronological order, starting hopefully from birth, and fixing them in a permanent way, e.g. with a treasury tag, so that new continuation cards can be easily added

- keeping hospital records, copies of GPs' letters and any other correspondence in chronological order and fastened together

- dealing with the results of any investigations in the same way

- keeping a summary sheet where the major and significant diseases or allergies are entered. This should be kept in the front of the medical record envelope (MRE)

- keeping prescription summary cards which are also useful as a permanent, easily seen record of all drugs prescribed

- there are many other forms of record card that can be used for specific purposes, such as the child immunization card, repeat prescription summary, obstetric record, contraceptive record, etc.

Medical receptionists and secretaries should not discard anything from a medical record envelope without the doctor's permission.

Storage of medical records

There are different ways of grouping medical records and different types of records. The most commonly used record is the small size medical record envelope (7 in. × 5½ in.) or the A4-size folder.

Some practices separate male and female records, but the majority file them together. There may be occasions when families are filed together in an A4 family folder. Every practice has its own system, but there are three main methods of storage:

1 *Lateral* shelving where records are placed side-by-side on shelves in alphabetical order, with alphabetical guides.
2 *Vertical* filing in multi-drawer cabinets which should have alphabetical guides on the outside of the drawers.
3 *Carousel* or rotary filing cabinets.

A tracer or marker card should always be inserted whenever a file is pulled, and removed once the medical record is back in place. The receptionist or secretary should always check to see whether a new continuation sheet is required for doctors to record their findings.

Whatever system of filing is used in the practice, accurate filing is essential. It should be possible to pull and refile records quickly and accurately.

Confidentiality of medical records

The medical record itself has a statement at the bottom saying it is the property of the Department of Health. However, the protection of the contents for purposes of confidentiality is the responsibility of the doctor and practice staff. Secretaries and receptionists must adhere to the rules of the practice established by the doctor as to who may access the information contained in the records.

Practice staff must never divulge any information contained in medical records and great care must be taken to ensure their safe custody. Remember, many people call into the practice and may be able to see over the reception counter and read things upside down. Cleaners and maintenance people may come into the practice when letters and other confidential information are left lying around.

There are certain legal issues appertaining to access to medical records, and data protection; these are explained fully in Chapter 4.

Much information about patients, their medical history, investigations, prescribing records, etc., are now stored on computer, but the principles of confidentiality still apply.

The medical record and information systems in general practice

The medical record is an important part of the overall information system for general practice. The record serves the needs of:

- preventive medicine
- at-risk groups of patients
- quality control measures – patient recall, performance review
- practice planning – administration and finance
- education – doctor, staff, trainee and patients
- research.

The age–sex register

The practice population can be well served by an age–sex register, either a manual system or computerized, to help identify patients at risk.

An age–sex register can be used for:

- child health surveillance
- child immunization uptake
- cervical cytology uptake
- geriatric screening (over 75s)
- hypertensive, diabetic, asthmatic patient screening (at-risk and chronic disease groups)
- health promotion
- an age–sex profile of the practice.

Disease or diagnostic index

Once again, the system of identification of patients who have certain diseases may be either maintained manually or stored as computer data. In its simplest form in a manual system, the notes can be colour-tagged according to the system established by the Royal College of General Practitioners, who have identified eight disease groups, for example:

- Red – sensitivities
- Brown – diabetes
- Yellow – epilepsy
- Green – tuberculosis

- Blue – hypertension
- White – long-term maintenance therapy
- Black – attempted suicide
- Black and white chequered – measles.

The presence of a coloured tag means that the disorder is, or has been, present; the absence of a tag can never imply the absence of such a disorder.

The medical records of deceased patients can either be sent back immediately to the health authority, or await their request for return of medical records. However, this procedure may change in the near future as many medical practices are directly linked to health authorities by computer, and such procedures can be carried out by computerized systems.

7

The hospital service

The patient's route through the hospital

The process begins with a visit, by the patient, either to their GP, or to an accident and emergency department (A&E), or to one of the few direct access services offered by some hospitals, for example walk-in clinics for genitourinary medicine. A GP visit results in a referral, leading to an out-patient appointment, a place on a waiting list and then admission. A direct visit to the hospital may result in a waiting list place or even immediate admission, with the GP being informed afterwards. Once in the hospital, the patient may be treated as an inpatient or a day case, with access as necessary to diagnostic services, operating theatres or treatment departments.

On discharge a summary of treatment given and follow-up needed is given to the patient's GP. Community support may be arranged, and follow-up clinic appointments may take place, either in the GP's surgery or back at the hospital itself, before the patient is fully discharged (Figure 7.1)

Outpatient appointments

A referral letter or specially designed referral form is sent by the GP to the appropriate consultant with an outline of the patient's condition. In exceptional circumstances, a telephone referral can be made. The consultant decides how urgent the case is, and when the patient should be seen. A letter or form is sent to the patient with details of the appointment.

If a patient has failed to turn up for a hospital appointment this is drawn to the attention of the consultant who decides whether another appointment is to be sent or whether the GP is to be informed first.

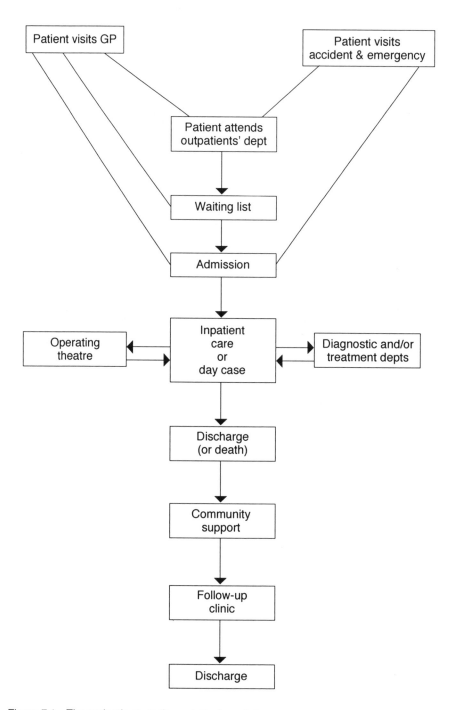

Figure 7.1   The patient's route through the hospital.

Outpatient appointments may be made centrally, or in each department, or in a mix of both. In many hospitals the system is computerized. Each consultant generally decides how appointments are made, whether in blocks or singly, the amount of time allocated to each patient, how many new and how many follow-up patients are to be booked in each clinic.

Referrals need not always be from a GP, but can be from the hospital's own A&E department, from another clinic, transferred from another consultant during or after treatment, or from another hospital.

Preparing for clinics

When preparing for a clinic, the first task is to ensure that the patient's notes are ready for doctors to refer to during the consultation. The importance of this cannot be over-stressed, since missing or incomplete notes will result in serious difficulties for the doctor and delays for the patient. It is sensible to allow as much time as possible.

Clinic lists will be available from the appointment book, or computerized patient administration system, showing all those due to attend. Case notes are then retrieved, or 'pulled', double-checking for the right patient using not only name but date of birth and hospital or NHS number. Checks are made that results of tests and other investigations, X-rays, etc., which were ordered after the previous visit are available.

Receiving patients

When a visitor arrives at reception you should go through the following stages:

- Smile and greet them courteously.

- Establish their identity and the reason for their visit.

- If the visitor has arrived at the wrong clinic in a busy hospital, give them clear and accurate directions and, wherever possible, provide them with an escort. This is particularly important if they are confused or distressed.

- If the visitor is a patient booked into clinic ask them to take a seat and explain to them:

    – which doctor will see them
    – how long they are likely to have to wait
    – where they can obtain refreshments
    – where the toilet is situated.

- Deal patiently and cheerfully with any queries the patient might have, and if you can't answer their questions yourself find someone (e.g. a nurse) who can.

- If there is likely to be any delay in the patient being seen, try to find out how long this is expected to be and give the patient a diplomatic and apologetic explanation.

- If the patient has language difficulties, obtain an interpreter or linkworker.

You should always be aware that the visitor may be experiencing discomfort or may be worried about the visit. This should be taken into account in all dealings with patients, their relatives and friends.

Admissions from the waiting list

Admissions from the waiting list (elective admissions) are usually handled by an admissions office, which is also responsible for keeping an accurate bed state for the entire hospital. Beds are not occupied at all times, although the hospital will try to maintain occupancy to the maximum to make best use of resources. Elective admissions will fill a portion of beds, but there must be the space and flexibility to be able to accommodate unforeseen demands. A pattern will have emerged over time, and the hospital will plan the use of its beds accordingly.

Admissions on to wards for day case treatment, to day surgery, or for the delivery of babies may be booked direct by those departments. Lists of expected admissions are given to each ward daily, and copied to the records department so that case notes are made available.

Accident and emergency admissions

When a patient is brought in to A&E by ambulance, the drivers will pass on whatever information they have obtained, and the receptionist will check what previous records exist for that patient. Treatment will not be delayed for this information if it is urgently needed. Particular procedures are followed if the patient is a road traffic accident victim, where ambulance transport costs are recovered, usually from the driver's insurance. Special arrangements also exist for suspected non-accidental injury of a child.

Every hospital has its own procedure for major accidents, and will rehearse it in conjunction with the emergency services, from time to time.

Follow-up after admission

When a patient is discharged from hospital the medical staff prepare a form for the patient to hand to their GP. A form is also completed for financial purposes, showing the diagnosis and any operations performed. After discharge a full summary is sent to the GP.

Not all patients leave the hospital alive. Following the death of a patient, the relatives must, of course, be dealt with in a kind and sensitive manner.

Home from hospital support

An increasing number of hospitals are finding that a patient can be discharged more successfully if offered support at home for a period of time following their return. Home from hospital teams consist of trained nurses and care support staff, who arrange to visit frequently and regularly over a specified period to help the patient adjust to being back at home. Help is offered with a range of activities designed to increase the patient's confidence in being able to cope at home. A speedier and more successful discharge both helps the patient and keeps acute hospital beds available for those who need acute nursing care.

Day cases and ward attendees

More and more people opt for surgery as a day case, where this is possible. Strict criteria apply and not all procedures, or all patients, can be dealt with in this way. Every effort is made to ensure that the patient has someone to collect them at the end of the day. An overnight stay will always be available should the patient's condition require it.

Most hospitals have taken steps to increase the proportion of work done on a day case basis, but interestingly, the assumption frequently made by patients that this is a cheaper option for the NHS is not often borne out. Many hospitals find that variable costs, for tests, disposables, etc. are higher per patient, and since they will be putting more patients through each bed, one per day rather than, for example, one per two or three days, total costs for these items can escalate. Staff costs can be higher because of the greater dependency of each patient, and the fixed costs associated with the building are not reduced until there has been a major shift from inpatients to day cases, allowing ward closures and large staff reductions.

The hospital team

Hospital staff fall into a number of professional groups, as follows:

Medical staff

- *Consultants* are responsible for the diagnosis and treatment of patients referred to them.

- *Junior doctors in training*, house officers, senior house officers and specialist registrars work for a consultant's firm. Although they are qualified doctors, they are in training for specialist roles.

- *Other doctors*, such as staff grades, clinical assistants, hospital practitioners and associate specialists are also attached to a consultant's firm. They are below consultant grade but are no longer in training.

Nursing staff

- *Nurses and midwives* carry out the regular care for patients as set out in the care plan, and administer drugs and treatment under the direction of the doctor. Psychiatric nurses work to ensure patients' mental health. Midwives care for mothers and babies and have special status as independent practitioners, which allows them in certain circumstances to practise without a doctor's prior instruction.

- *Health care assistants* and nursing assistants work with qualified nurses and therapists to deliver non-technical care to patients.

- *Nurse practitioners* are nurses with specific training to allow them to practise independently, in some cases taking on responsibilities usually held by junior doctors. They may run clinics, assess priorities in A&E departments (known as triage) and undertake some treatments.

Therapy staff

- *Physiotherapists* diagnose and treat patients' difficulties with movement and rehabilitation after illness or injury, using exercises, manipulation and a range of equipment.

- *Occupational therapists* help patients to resume a normal life through activity based treatments, and the provision of aids to living, such as special tools and appliances.

- *Dieticians* advise patients and other care staff on the best food and drink for particular conditions. They also advise on intravenous and other drip feeding procedures.

- *Speech and language therapists* help patients with communication difficulties, especially after a stroke or other injury to the head, throat or chest. They also treat children who have communication difficulties.

- *Hearing therapists* assist patients with hearing difficulties and support those with hearing aids.

- *Pharmacists* provide specialist advice on appropriate drug treatments, including drug interactions, and supply drugs to inpatients and outpatients.

Diagnostic staff

- *Pathology* staff carry out a range of tests which are grouped into categories. Haematology staff carry out tests on blood, cytology staff study the nature of cells, especially cancerous or other diseased ones. Histology staff study tissues to detect disease. Microbiology staff test urine, faeces and other body fluids for parasites and bacteria, virology staff look for the presence of viruses, and chemistry staff look for the presence of chemicals which may cause illness or be a symptom of disease.

- *Radiography* staff take X-rays, for interpretation by a radiologist. They carry out various treatments, such as barium meals or dye injections, to show up particular parts of the body. They also use ultrasound to examine babies in the womb, and to detect disease, such as a tumour, in other parts of the body. Computerized axial tomography (CAT) scanning uses a computer to reconstruct an image of a layer of tissue in the body. Nuclear magnetic resource imaging (NMRI) uses radio frequency radiation and a magnetic field to produce anatomical sections of the body.

- *ECG* staff use an electrocardiograph to take readings which describe the functioning of a patient's heart, for cardiologists to interpret.

- *EEG* staff use an electroencephalograph to produce a picture of brain activity, placing small electrodes on the patient's head to measure electrical impulses. Consultants in EEG interpret the pictures.

Support workers

- *Non-clinical support departments* include chaplaincy, catering, cleaning, porters, security, building, engineering, linen and laundry, and transport.

Management and administration

- *Management departments* include the chief executive's team, general managers, directors of nursing and midwifery, business managers, human resources, finance, payroll, information and marketing.

- *Administrative support* is provided by admissions, registry and medical records.

Clinical audit

The term clinical audit embraces the audit activity of all health care professionals, including nurses, doctors and other health care staff. It is a widely used tool within hospitals, and is defined as the systematic and critical analysis of the quality of clinical care, including the procedures used for diagnosis, treatment and care, the associated resources and the resulting outcome and quality of life for the patient.

As a general principle, audit should be professionally led, and should focus on improving outcomes. It will have greatest impact if it forms part of routine clinical care. It should be seen as an educational process, and be an important part of quality programmes. It must respect confidentiality at the individual patient or clinician level and take into consideration the views of the patient and their carers.

What is a medical record?

A medical record is the history of a patient's treatment as an outpatient or inpatient, or both, at a particular hospital. If it is known that a patient has attended another hospital, a copy of that treatment record should be included in the current hospital medical record. A complete record prevents duplication and facilitates future care. In most cases, at present, the most complete medical records are the GP's notes as they follow patients as they move around. GP records should also contain details of any hospital treatment received by the patient, as well as any letters and summaries from hospitals which the patient may have attended.

Why have medical records in hospitals?

- The medical record is of most value in the treatment of patients, as a reminder and as a means of communication to doctors, nurses, etc. of what has been given and with what effect; and investigations which have been made and the results.

- They are an educational instrument and as such are used to teach medical students, nurses and other students.

- They are used for research.

Storage of medical records

Every hospital has its own system, but there are three main methods:

- lateral filing systems – files are side by side on shelves
- vertical filing systems – files are stored in multidrawer cabinets
- rotary (carousel) systems.

Each of these methods has advantages and disadvantages. Security of any area in which medical records are held is of prime importance.

Case notes

Although medical records were standardized when the NHS was instituted in order to ensure uniformity of record-keeping procedures, these vary from hospital to hospital. A hospital receptionist or medical secretary who moves from one hospital to another is unlikely to find herself handling exactly the same procedures. Standardization overall does exist but without rigidity.

Case notes basically follow the same pattern everywhere, being contained in A4-sized folders and consisting of five sections:

- identification
- medical
- nursing
- correspondence
- results, e.g. pathology tests, X-rays.

Identification section

This section allows space for the following information:

- hospital's name and code number, which is usually printed
- patient's name, address, status, telephone number
- patient's postcode
- date of birth
- GP information
- consultant
- hospital number
- occupation
- religion
- NHS number
- next of kin information.

Medical section

This section is for doctors' use only, and generally consists of:

- history of present complaint
- past medical history (PMH)

- family history
- patient complains of (PCO)
- on examination (OE)
- differential diagnosis
- investigations
- treatment.

Nursing section

This section contains the observations of nursing staff (recorded only when patients are admitted):

- nursing record
- temperature, pulse, respiration (TPR) – graphic records on special sheets. Also used for blood pressure, micturition and bowel function
- intake and output charts (record of all fluids taken orally or by transfusion and excreted).

Correspondence section

This section will usually include:

- GP's referral letter or proforma referral
- consultant's reports to GP
- letters to and from other consultants or other professionals.

Other information

The records may also contain:

- prescription charge
- social history
- theatre/surgical operation sheet

- consent form
- anaesthetic form.

The order of all these sheets inside the folder will vary from hospital to hospital, and ideally the order is printed either on the front or inside the cover. Each section of the case notes is generally filed in chronological order.

Master index

In theory, each patient should have only one medical record. This rule is broken by the law which states that the records of patients who attend the genitourinary clinics must be kept apart from any other medical records belonging to such patients. Also, psychiatric medical records of patients are usually kept separately with just a note placed in the main medical record stating where and when the patient attended for psychiatric care. In order to reduce the number of patients with several medical records, a master index is kept.

The master index is an alphabetical list of patients who have attended the hospital. It can be kept on cards and filed manually, on microfiche, on computer, on microfilm or on optic disc. The information recorded is usually basic: surname, forename(s), sex, date of birth, home address, marital status, sometimes date of first attendance and consultants seen, religion, date of death, patient index number.

The master index record for the accident and emergency and the emergency eye departments usually consists of alphabetically filed cards of attendees there.

Filing room/medical records library

This is the hub of the medical records department. It is often in a lower ground or ground floor because of the weight of all the records. Security in this area is of prime importance: unauthorized access cannot be allowed.

Within the library, files will be organized within a strict system. A number of different filing systems exist as follows, although in most hospitals medical records are filed by patient master index number. Colour coding is often used to prevent misfiling.

Master index number – terminal digit (12 34 **56**)

Six numbers are required. 12 34 56 gives 56 as the terminal digit, 34 as the middle digit and 12 as the first digit. Divide the main area into 100 sections, 00 to 99, and these divisions give the foundation for terminal digit filing. This means that 56 will be in main section 56. The main sections are again divided into another 00 to 99 subsections, so 56 will be placed in subsection 34 and 12 will be placed behind 11 and before 13 in subsection 34. Though this may sound complicated, with a little practice it is easy to work and helps to cut down misfiling.

Middle digit (12 **34** 56)

A similar process to terminal digit is followed, but the numbers are followed in a different order.

* Straight numeric (1,2,3, etc.)
* Date of birth – alphabetic
* Surname – alphabetic.

Medical records procedures for departments

Accident and emergency records

If a patient arrives in hospital by emergency ambulance, the drivers will fill in the ambulance book giving what information about the patient they have collected. A receptionist will check if there are previous accident and emergency records and/or medical records, and will obtain them as quickly as possible. Treatment does not wait until these are found. If there is no record of previous attendance an A&E record is started with what information is available. This may be difficult if the patient is unconscious and unaccompanied, so there must be a follow-up should the patient eventually go onto a ward. Nurses usually record any property the patient is carrying, but a receptionist could be asked to do so, with a witness.

If the medical record shows that the patient has current appointments for outpatients, or has been booked for admission, or for theatre, these departments must be informed if the patient is not going to attend.

Outpatients records

Outpatients attend the hospital after a letter of referral from their GP. Many GPs use a referral form. This gives basic details of the patient which help to find any existing medical records. The letters go to the consultant or senior registrar of the department concerned and an appointment is given according to urgency. A list for each clinic is drawn up, and the medical records for all patients booked are then prepared.

A copy of the manual list or the computer list in 'pulling' order is produced. 'Pulling' is jargon for the actual gathering together of medical records from the filing shelves. Filing room staff, clinic clerks, receptionists or admission office staff may do this; again, this depends on each hospital's system.

The person preparing for the clinic will receive a copy of the list, and must obtain the medical records and laboratory tests, X-rays, etc. which were ordered at the previous visit. These results must be in the medical records and the X-rays ordered so that they are at the clinic. The medical records are also checked to ensure that there is paper on which the medical staff may write, and are 'stamped' or written up with the date and consultant of the clinic.

When the patient is new to the hospital the case notes are partially written up (in order to save paper and time) but details are not confirmed on the computer until the patient has actually arrived. On arrival all the patient details are checked and any missing information is obtained. Where a manual system is used this information is put on the master index card.

Day case records

These are usually handled by the department or the ward concerned. The medical records department is contacted for the necessary records before the patient arrives, where possible. The procedure is broadly the same as that described above for outpatients.

Maternity records

In many hospitals these records are retained by the woman throughout her pregnancy and only kept by the hospital after confinement.

Admissions and transfers

Lists of expected admissions are sent to each ward daily. A copy of this list is sent to the records library so that the medical records can be on the wards before the patient is admitted. Usually the ward receptionist does the check on the contents of the medical records, as described above for outpatients.

Retention of records

paediatric	25 years
mothers/babies	25 years
psychiatric	25 years
all others	8 years

The role of the secretary in hospital

The vital link

The secretary's role is a vital one in the smooth running of the department. Frequently the first point of contact, the secretary acts as representative of those for whom she works, and also represents the whole organization. She provides a link between members of the health care team, and between them and the outside world, and her involvement can ensure that scarce resources, such as a consultant's time or a theatre list, are used as efficiently as possible, and to the very best advantage. Diplomat, oiler of wheels, the one who gets things done, the one who remembers that important detail that everyone else has forgotten, the role is as varied as it is complex.

Core knowledge and skills

All secretarial posts in health care services require a body of core knowledge and skills which underpin all activities within the job. These include good interpersonal skills, respect for confidentiality, the ability to use appropriate medical terms, an understanding of the principles of medical ethics and etiquette, and sensitivity to the physical and psychological needs of patients and their carers.

In addition to these, there is a requirement to comply with legal requirements concerning working practices, and to be aware of and work within other health and safety regulations.

Key result areas

The role of each individual will vary, and the emphasis given to different parts of each job will be different, but the following key result areas are common to most:

COMMUNICATIONS	Processing, distribution and despatch of mail. Efficient and courteous use of communications systems, including telephone, answering machines, pagers, fax, telex and electronic mail.
CORRESPONDENCE	Identifying, prioritizing and responding to correspondence for own action, including letters, circulars, invoices and statements. Passing on correspondence for others' attention promptly.
ORGANIZING WORK SCHEDULES	Maintaining diaries, visual planners, computerized and other scheduling aids. Making and confirming appointments. Planning and prioritizing own work schedule. Co-ordinating assistance where necessary.
INFORMATION	Using manual and computerized filing systems. Responding to requests for and producing information from internal and external sources, including public documents, timetables and statistics. Presenting information in different formats.
OFFICE ADMINISTRATION	Managing and controlling office stock, following appropriate ordering procedures. Dealing with faulty equipment. Maintaining a petty cash system.
MEETINGS	Preparing and producing agenda papers and minutes. Booking rooms, refreshments and audio-visual aids. Arranging room layout. Attending meetings to take notes, and producing formal records of business undertaken.

RECEPTION	Receiving and screening visitors, and assisting them wherever possible.
DOCUMENTS AND REPORTS	Preparing and producing documents, including reports, tables and statistics. Arranging copying, collating and binding.
APPOINTMENT SYSTEMS	Answering requests for and allocating appointments. Following booking-in procedures, registration procedures, preparing case notes, paperwork, tests, results, etc. for clinics or surgical lists.
WAITING LISTS	Accurately compiling and prioritizing of waiting lists, manual or computerized. Arranging and confirming appointments, handling queries and undertaking follow-up action as necessary.
HEALTH AND SAFETY	Ensuring the work area is kept free from hazards. Recording and reporting accidents and unsafe features. Following safe methods for lifting and handling heavy or bulky items. Following procedures for raising the alarm or summoning assistance. Adhering to procedures for handling specimens.
PATIENT CARE AND SUPPORT	Dealing with patients and carers with sensitivity, identifying and responding to their needs. Adhering to the requirements of the Patient's Charter. Arranging transport and escorts, following procedures for handling patients' property.

Private medicine

8

Introduction

Throughout the development of the National Health Service, the private care sector continued to operate and remained a minor element of the total health provision, until the 1980s when it rapidly expanded in response to the various constraints on the NHS. Both the number of health insurance schemes and private providers have expanded and by 1989, 13% of the population in the UK was covered by private medical insurance, and approximately 17% of all inpatients were treated privately and 17% of elective surgery was carried out in the private sector. At the same time there has been an increase in the number of private residential and nursing homes.

A number of medical secretaries and receptionists are now employed in private medicine, either working for specialist physicians or surgeons in their consulting rooms, or in a private clinic or hospital.

Although, essentially, their function is similar to secretaries and receptionists working in NHS organizations, there are certain differences in working practice (see Chapters 6 and 7).

Private clinic or hospital

Patient contact and communication

Receptionists welcome patients on arrival at the clinic or hospital, where they may be asked to complete registration forms. They will then direct them to the appropriate departments which include:

- outpatients

- physiotherapy

- X-ray/imaging

- pathology.

They may take telephone calls from patients, give advice on payment protocol, make an appointment for them to see a consultant or other health care professional and, if necessary, refer to a nurse for advice.

Facilities

Private hospitals and clinics provide patients with rooms equipped to the highest standards to ensure a relaxed and comfortable environment, which is conducive to rapid recovery and convalescence. Rooms are generally equipped with en suite bathroom facilities, as well as telephone and colour television. Other amenities available will probably include:

- library

- mail, fax and secretarial services

- counsellor (for patients and their families)

- hairdressing and laundry services

- chiropody

- private ambulances.

Private hospitals offer a wide range of menus, designed with 'healthy eating' in mind and which form a nutritionally balanced diet. Light refreshments are usually available for visitors.

Operating theatres and diagnostic and treatment departments are usually equipped to the highest standards and use the latest technology. Resident medical officers provide 24 hour medical cover for patients.

Customer care

Customer care is always an important element in a private clinic. For example, tea or coffee is offered free of charge to patients waiting in outpatients.

In an effort to improve the quality of care, receptionists will present questionnaires to patients, who are asked to comment on all aspects of their care through the outpatient department including reception, nursing, X-ray, phlebotomy, etc.

Other aspects of customer care are the same as to be expected from a similar NHS organization, for example, arranging for a wheelchair or porter, and to generally help a patient as is felt necessary.

Quality assurance

Private medicine is a highly competitive market, and hospitals and clinics have accordingly developed quality assurance programmes to maintain and improve standards. Regular audits and reviews are held to monitor achievements against written standards. Patients' opinions and views are an integral part of performance audit. Staff training and development is generally included as initiatives contributing to providing expert care and attention to patients at all times.

Telephone skills

In common with other areas of medical practice, the receptionist in a private clinic or hospital deals with all types of people – elderly, vague people, overseas visitors who cannot speak English very well, impatient people, demanding people. Patience, tact, understanding and a good telephone manner are just as essential in a private setting, as well as the ability to deal with situations efficiently and quickly because there is always another call waiting to be dealt with!

Appointments

When patients make appointments, they are asked for the basic information:

- name (surname and forename(s))
- age, if necessary
- telephone number
- address
- whether they have medical insurance.

An appointment card is sent to the patient with directions on how to reach the clinic, and details of car parking availability. The patient is informed of consultation costs (if known) and the cost of any investigations.

Outpatient hospital/clinic registration procedure

Patients are asked to complete a registration form on arrival at reception, giving the following information:

- name, address, telephone number

- name of consultant

- method of payment, and may be asked to sign that they are willing to pay for their treatment on the day.

Inpatient registration

If a patient has to be admitted, a more detailed form is given to them for completion, which also asks for details of their insurance cover.

In some private clinics, patients may be encouraged to pay for outpatient treatment on the day of their appointment, and to get any insurance forms signed there and then by the consultant, so that there will be little or no delay in reimbursement.

Pathology and X-ray

Receptionists may generate accounts for patients attending for pathology and X-ray, and will request payment at the time of investigation.

Medical records

Consultants in a private hospital or clinic will bring patients' notes with them, and keep them in their personal possession.

The only records kept at the clinic will be screening records such as well-woman, executive screening, breast screening, etc. All records of work generated by the staff are retained at the clinic.

Mail – incoming and outgoing

Mail addressed to doctors is generally kept in pigeon-holes for their collection. All outgoing mail, accounts, letters, etc. are collected by the mail room at the end of the day for posting.

Patient accounts

Preparation and processing of patient accounts is a major part of the receptionist's job. They are prepared on the computer, and have to be ready for patients when they leave the clinic. Private hospitals and clinics have the facility to collect cash, accept payment by credit cards and cheques, and often have a 'Switch' machine.

Systems

All accounts for the day will be sent to a main accounts department for filing. Any outstanding bills can be demonstrated on the computer screen. There is a variety of software available, but a frequently used system is 'Compucare'.

Liaison with other health care professionals

Receptionists have regular contact with consultants and their secretaries, as well as with physiotherapy, X-ray and nursing staff at the clinic. They will have frequent telephone contact with almost every cross-section of the medical field, including laboratory staff, doctors, secretaries, NHS hospitals, clinics (private and NHS), psychologists, etc.

From time to time, they may be asked to contact a patient's private medical insurance company for information regarding levels of cover, etc.

Waiting areas and consulting rooms

Consulting rooms are checked and maintained by nursing staff, except for stationery items, which are the responsibility of the receptionists.

Doctors will usually liaise by telephone to ask for their patients to be taken to them, and the receptionist or nurse will show them into the doctors' rooms.

Waiting areas are kept clean and tidy by frequent visits from house-keepers. Catering staff will ensure a supply of tea and coffee and remove dirty cups from the waiting area. Magazines are always available for patients.

The secretary in private practice

The role of the secretary in private practice is a diverse and varied one, requiring qualities and skills additional to secretarial duties. In many instances, the secretary will be working on her own, apart from the days her consultant is seeing patients at the practice. This means that decisions of a non-medical nature may have to be made.

Reception and secretarial duties

A great deal of the secretary's time is involved with answering the telephone, dealing with patients' enquiries and making appointments.

Once an appointment is made for a new patient, a file is made up with basic patient information and details of private medical insurance cover, in readiness for the initial consultation.

The secretary may be asked by her consultant to organize investigations (pathology, radiological, etc.) for patients when necessary and to arrange for external referrals, for example physiotherapy, other consultants. Admission to hospital or clinic may also be arranged for the patient.

From time to time the secretary will need to liaise with her NHS counterpart, either to leave a message or to contact the consultant when he/she is working in the hospital department.

She will be responsible for keeping the consulting room, waiting room and her own office tidy and generally ensuring the comfort of patients while they wait to see the doctor.

Clerical duties

On a daily basis mail has to be sorted and incoming correspondence attended to as appropriate. Photocopying of insurance or medical reports may have to be done from time to time, and messages sent or received by facsimile (fax) transmission accordingly dealt with. Correspondence will have to be posted and a supply of postage stamps maintained at the practice.

The secretary will usually be responsible for petty cash to purchase office sundries and maintain supplies of stationery and other items.

Patients records will be pulled prior to consultation and checked that results of investigations previously requested are complete. Following consultation and any further action that has to be taken, the notes will be filed away.

Secretarial skills

Good secretarial skills are important, including typing and competent use of wordprocessing systems. Many consultants prefer to dictate their letters and reports onto a dictating machine, but some still prefer their secretaries to use shorthand. Usually, a combination of both shorthand and audiotyping is desirable.

A knowledge of medical terminology and medical abbreviations are always useful, but not necessarily essential. A good medical dictionary, common sense and an ability to learn the specialist terms will usually suffice.

In private practice, with no nurse in attendance, the secretary may find that she is asked to act as a chaperone during the consultant's examination of the patient.

Practice management

The secretary in private practice will find that in addition to her other duties she is also a practice manager. The good manager will update existing systems to ensure the practice operates effectively and in an efficient way. She will be responsible for sending patient accounts and, if necessary, will remind patients that settlement of their outstanding account is overdue, and will follow up unpaid accounts on a regular basis, as well as patient account reconciliation. Any long-standing overdue accounts will be referred to a debt collection agency when necessary.

The secretary will reconcile the petty cash account on a regular (usually monthly) basis, and recommend when accounts should be paid by the consultant.

Another financial aspect of the work of the medical secretary in private practice will, no doubt, be to operate a payroll (maybe for one person only), to calculate her own PAYE and NI contributions, and to make year end returns to the Inland Revenue. She will also be responsible for ordering any supplies necessary for the doctor's consulting room and her own office requirements.

Summary

It will be noted that the role of the receptionist and secretary in private practice is very much the same as working in an NHS organization.

An essential quality is to be able to deal with patients in an efficient yet sympathetic manner, and understand the emotions and concerns experienced by patients when entering a clinical environment. Although it is desirable for secretaries and receptionists to have a knowledge of medical terminology and other clinical aspects, a competent person will learn these as they carry out their day-to-day duties.

9

Forms, fees and finances in general practice

Introduction

General medical practice is a small business, like any other practice of professionals e.g. solicitors or accountants. Therefore there is a need to get money in to cover the costs of providing the service to patients. Figure 9.1 shows a list of expenses incurred in running a practice and a list of sources of income. The profit is the difference between income and expenditure, and it is from the profit that the partners take their drawings. It is therefore easy to understand why doctors insist that all claims for payments are made promptly and that expenses are kept down to a minimum.

The majority of the income is via the health authority/health board/ health and social services board, and in order to claim their share a practice has to complete a variety of forms – these are the equivalent of invoices for services given. Whilst some of the forms are filled in only when a partner joins a practice, or on an annual basis, the majority are completed as each service is rendered. Therefore, the receptionist is a key person in ensuring that forms are completed as patients enter or leave the premises. Figure 9.2 shows the items of income set against the staff members who may be responsible for ensuring the claim forms are completed.

Practices have a variety of ways of sharing out the clerical workload, and in larger practices it may be expedient to have one or two staff who take responsibility for checking that forms are completed and sent off to the health authority/health board/health and social services board on a regular basis. However, if all the receptionists are good at completing the forms accurately and completely, the task of batching and sending off becomes much easier and quicker.

Income

NHS   Practice allowance
Capitation   Registration
Child health surveillance
Deprivation
Items of service   Registration medical
Night visits
Maternity services
Emergency treatment
Immediately necessary treatment
Contraceptive services
Temporary residents
Adult vaccination/immunization
Minor surgery
Targets   Cervical cytology
Immunizations under 2s
Immunizations under 5s
Health promotion banding
Dispensing payments
Associate allowance
Seniority
Postgraduate education allowance
Trainee supervision grant
Medical students
Reimbursements   Trainee salary
Rent and rates
Staff salaries and NI
Staff training
Computer maintenance
Private   Private medical attendant reports
Insurance medicals
Cremation forms
Sundry   Passport forms
Travel vaccinations, e.g. yellow fever
PSV, HGV, elderly driver
Other appointments   Company or school medical officer
Police surgeon

Expenditure

Practice   Drugs and instruments
Hire and maintenance of equipment
Repairs and renewals
Premises   Rates and water rates
Heat and light
Insurance
Cleaning
Salaries   Staff
Trainee
Administration Postage
Stationery
Telephone
Professional fees   Accountant
Solicitor
Banking   Interest
Loan repayments

The turnover (i.e. all forms of income added together) of a large practice may be in excess of £500 000 whereas that of a small single-handed practice might be £90 000.

Figure 9.1   Practice income and expenditure.

Source of income	Item	Persons likely to complete the claim form			
		Receptionist	Clerk	Secretary	Manager
NHS	Practice allowance	automatic (only affected by change of partnership)			
	Capitation				
	Registration	✔	✔		
	Child health surveillance	✔	✔		
	Deprivation	automatic (depends upon post code)			
	Items of service				
	Registration medical	✔			
	Night visits	✔	✔		
	Maternity services	✔			
	Emergency treatment	✔			
	Immediately necessary treatment	✔			
	Contraceptive services	✔			
	Temporary residents	✔			
	Adult vaccination/ immunization	✔			
	Minor surgery	✔	✔		
	Targets				
	Cervical cytology	✔	✔		
	Immunizations under 2s	✔	✔		
	Immunizations under 5s	✔	✔		
	Health promotion banding		✔		✔
	Dispensing payments		✔		
	Associate allowance			✔	✔
	Seniority	automatic once set up			✔
	Postgraduate education allowance			✔	✔
	Trainee supervision grant				✔
	Medical students			✔	✔
	Reimbursements				
	Trainee salary				✔
	Rent and rates			✔	✔
	Staff salaries and NI				✔
	Staff training				✔
	Computer maintenance				✔
Private	Private medical attendant reports			✔	✔
	Insurance medicals			✔	
	Cremation forms			✔	
	Sundry				
	Passport forms	✔			
	Travel vaccinations, e.g. yellow fever	✔			
	PSV, HVG, elderly driver	✔			
	Other appointments				
	Company or school medical officer			✔	
	Police surgeon			✔	

Figure 9.2   Income in general practice and the role of the receptionist.

Most practices have systems for ensuring that forms are filled in at the right time. These will range from stickers on the outside of the medical record, through cardex boxes (manual recording) to computer generated lists and reminder messages on the computer screen when a patient record is opened. The introduction of health authority/GP links project where claims can be sent automatically to the health authority/health board/health and social services board will eventually make the paper claims redundant.

Regardless of the system of claiming it is important that receptionists are aware of what claims should be made under what circumstances. Various publications exist to give information on capitation, item of service claims, targets and payments to doctors. The most important is the Red Book – the Statement of Fees and Allowances. This is a loose-leaf document, which is updated as rates of pay, conditions regulating payments, or other changes are made, and the health authority/health board/health and social services board base their decisions regarding payments on its content. Every partner and trainee GP in a practice is issued with their own copy of the Red Book, and every surgery needs to have a copy available to receptionists who want to check what is payable and when. Furthermore, it is essential that all copies of the Red Book are kept up to date, so that when the latest statement of fees and allowances (SFA) (amendment to the Red Book) is issued the new pages are appropriately filed into place and the old versions disposed of.

To understand what can be claimed under which circumstances there is no real substitute for reading the Red Book and clarifying queries with the health authority/health board/health and social services board. Many health authorities/health boards run short courses so that surgery staff can learn what the forms are for, how they should be completed, when to return them to the health authority/health board, and so on. Alternatively, it is possible to make an appointment to go to the health authority/health board/health and social services board to meet the staff who deal with claims. The receptionist who has made friends with people in the health authority/health board/health and social services board with whom regular contact has to be made is most likely to be able to submit claims accurately, promptly and keep abreast of trends and changes. There are so many changes affecting both surgeries and health authorities/health boards/health and social services boards these days that 'networking' is an essential activity.

In the surgery a collection of claim forms can be put into a folder along with brief details of when claims should be made, notes on completing the forms, and in-house systems for recording 'due to sign again' dates. This is a useful in-house reference source and training tool for new staff. However, as and when changes are made to claims it is important to ensure that the folder is updated.

It is important when handling claim forms and target sheets to be systematic, and therefore it is preferable not to work on reception duties at the same time, trying to squeeze in the paperwork between other tasks.

Paperwork takes a different set of skills to those used in receiving patients. If a receptionist works a busy morning shift on the reception desk it will be almost impossible to switch from pressured reception duties to calmly working through a pile of papers without a transitionary period – cup of coffee, pop out to the shops for fresh air, a chat, to wind down from the pressure.

RECEPTION DESK DUTIES	CLERICAL DUTIES
Require the ability to juggle many important priorities all at one time	Require a systematic orderly approach
Answering the telephone, controlling surgery flow and dealing with queries are 'demand driven' activities	Processing massive piles of paper requires self motivation – 'self driven'

Practice income

Income to the practice is derived from NHS sources, and from private sources, e.g. item of service claim forms come via the NHS, medical attendant reports for insurance companies are a private source (see Figure 9.1).

The fees payable for NHS payments are shown in the Red Book and the BMA recommends fees for private services. Both these sets of fees are summarized and displayed in tabular form in the doctor's weekly or monthly magazines and journals.

It is important that all sources of income are properly documented and claimed. The role of the receptionist cannot be underestimated in ensuring that services given are recorded and claimed for. The receptionist is the person who deals with the patients, is aware of what the doctor says he/she has done for a specific patient, and therefore is the pivotal person to ensure that claims are made or invoices are raised. The receptionist may not be required to do these tasks but to ensure that someone else has the necessary information to be able to do so.

However, there will be occasions when a receptionist is asked to advise a patient of what payment is required, to receive the payment and issue a receipt. Information about current fees should be kept readily to hand, along with printed receipts that need only to have name of patient, service given, date, amount paid and signature filled in by hand. The payment should then be passed to the appropriate person for banking.

Although most doctors are aware that private fees are a significant supplement to their income, some are reluctant to talk to patients about the fee for their services. Also staff should be aware that sums received from patients, great and small, cheque or cash, must all be passed through the practice accounts. Private fees are not a 'perk' – the Inland Revenue have been known to trace payments back over a number of years and claim back tax on them.

As in all the other aspects of general medical practice, the receptionist has a vital role to play in the financial success of a practice by cutting down on unnecessary wastage and expense, and ensuring that all income is claimed and processed promptly.

Helpful hints in completing health authority/health board claim forms

The following information should help you in completing any claim forms for which you are responsible in your practice.

Fewer better forms

On 1 July 1996 four new forms for the registration of family doctor services and items of service claims replaced 19 old forms. Their introduction was a result of the NHS scrutiny into bureaucracy in primary care, described in the NHS report *Patients not Paper*.

The report found that general medical practices were overburdened by excessive paper work. Contained in the 65 recommendations were proposals for a radical reduction in the number of forms required by general medical practices and health authorities to process patient registration and items of service claims.

The new forms and procedures were extensively piloted in England and Wales. In response to comments from the pilot authorities and practices a number of changes were incorporated into the design of the forms. Logical, user friendly and multi-purpose, they can readily be used with a minimum of training.

The forms are purchased in bulk by health authorities and supplied free of charge to practices. They are used throughout England and Wales. (Welsh language versions are available for GMS1 and GMS2). There are no local variations of the form and no locally produced versions of the national form.

The forms

The four forms are:

- GMS1 – Family doctor services registration
- GMS2 – Maternity medical services
- GMS3 – Temporary services
- GMS4 – Items of service multi-claims.

There is an optional envelope, the **GMS/E**, which can be used for submitting claims.

Health authority/general practitioner electronic Links

Practices electronically linked for registration only, use all the forms retaining **GMS1** as their record of the 'contract' to supply services.

Practices electronically linked for items of service continue to use GMS1, GMS2 and GMS3. GMS4 is used for those services not yet incorporated into the electronic Links.

GMS1: Family doctor services registration (Figure 9.3)

To be used:

- for application to join a family doctor's list by a patient, child or someone who is unable to complete the form themselves
- for an application for a child to register for child health surveillance
- for an application to join the NHS organ donor register.

This form replaces FP1, FP13, FP58, FP/CHS and DISP1.

At the practice

❶ *Child health surveillance* – the form can be used for child health surveillance claims only. Under these circumstances no patient's signature is required.

❷ *Patient's signature* – if the forms are completed on behalf of the patient by the doctor or practice staff, ask patient/patient representative to check all entries before signing **GMS1**. This signature should only be requested on completion of the form.

Figure 9.3   Family doctor services registration – Form GMS1.

❸ *NHS organ donor registration* – explain purpose of registration, pointing out that, in the event of a patient's death, relatives' permission would be asked. If patients are undecided give patient the NHS organ donor register leaflet for their further consideration. There is no upper or lower age limit and the signature may be that of the patient or the patient's representative.

❹ *HA code* – the GP's unique identifying code assigned to him/her by the health authority (HA).

❺ *Authorized signature* – ensure that the declaration is read before signing.

❻ *Practice stamp* – space for practice stamp or for entering name of practice.

All GMS1 forms can be submitted to the GP's responsible HA. At the HA, GMS1 forms received from practices for patients who live in neighbouring authorities are forwarded to those authorities for processing.

   If electronically linked, retain the form for nine months at the practice, otherwise send to the HA.

GMS2: Maternity medical services (Figure 9.4)

Use this for the patient's application to register with the family or other GP for maternity medical services. This form replaces FP24 and FP24A.

At the practice

❶ *Patient's signature* – if forms are completed on behalf of the patient by the doctor or practice staff ask patient/patient's representative to check all entries before signing GMS2. This signature should only be requested on completion of the form.

The patient's signature may be omitted if treatment is given in circumstances (such as a miscarriage) where the doctor considers it necessary in the patient's interest not to ask for her signature. In this case, the doctor should tick the appropriate box on the reverse of the form.

❷ *HA code* – the GPs unique identifying code assigned to him or her by the HA.

❸ *Booking date* – the booking date is the date of the doctors acceptance.

❹ *Authorised signature* – ensure that the declaration is read before signing.

❺ *Practice stamp* – space for the practice stamp or for entering name of practice.

Figure 9.4   Maternity medical services – Form GMS2.

The forms should be submitted to the GP's responsible HA. At the HA, GMS2 forms received from practices for patients who live elsewhere will be forwarded to those authorities for processing.

If electronically linked for items of service, retain the form for two years at the practice, otherwise send to the HA.

GMS3: Temporary services (Figure 9.5)

Use this form for all claims for non-registered patients except those receiving minor surgery and maternity medical services. This form replaces FP19, FP106, FP32 and FP1003 and is used in place of FP81, FP82 and FP73 for non-registered patients. The form is carbonized to allow for the duplication of patient details and space is provided on the reverse for clinical records which can be forwarded to the patient's home GP. This is a multi-claim form and can be used for more than one service per form but only for one patient.

At the practice

❶ *Doctor to whom details of treatment given should be sent* – in the case of armed services personnel this space should be used to record the current medical centre.

❷ *Authorized signature* – ensure that the declaration is read before signing.

❸ *Practice stamp* – space for the practice stamp or for entering name of practice.

❹ *Clinical records* – use the space provided to record details of treatment given, including if appropriate the type of vaccination/immunization. These details will be passed on to the patient's home doctor.

❺ *In case of queries* – enter the name of the doctor who should be contacted in case of queries by the patient's home doctor and enter the practice address or stamp.

❻ Do not write on this area as it will effect legibility of patient's details on reverse of form.

Note: Patient's signature is not required on GMS3.

If electronically linked for items of service, retain for 2 years, otherwise send to the HA.

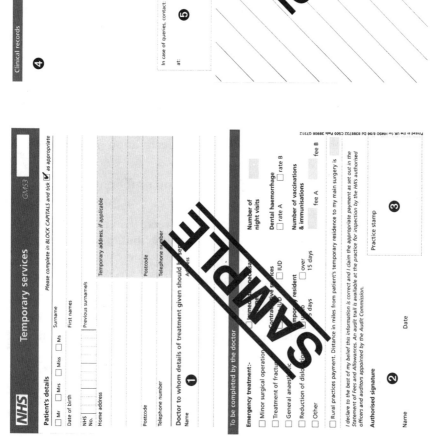

Figure 9.5   Temporary services – Form GMS3.

GMS4: Items of service multi-claim (Figure 9.6)

This form is used to claim for registration examination, night consultation, vaccinations and immunizations, contraceptive services, minor surgery, anaesthetic or dental haemorrhage. This replaces FP31, FP81, FP82, FP73, FP1001, FP1002. For non-registered patients use the form GMS3, except in the case of minor surgery.

At the practice

❶ *Item of service* – tick relevant box next to one item of service, then use this form **only** for the item ticked.

❷ *Date* – enter the date of examination, visit, acceptance, renewal or procedure.

❸ *Patient's name, date of birth and NHS number* – enter for all claims **except** minor surgery. To help speed payment enter date of birth and NHS number.

❹ The columns A and B are used to identify appropriate fee types:

- Vaccinations and immunizations: enter number of items in column A or B for appropriate fee band

- Contraceptive services: tick column A for non-IUD/tick column B for IUD/for continuous claims enter 'C' instead of a tick in column A or B

- Minor surgery: claims must be grouped in fives and patient's name and details should be omitted. Enter procedure code in column A:

  I = injection; A = aspiration; N = incision; E = excision; C = cautery; O = other.

- Dental haemorrhage: enter a tick in column A or B for appropriate rate band.

❺ *HA column* – enter the HA in whose area the patient lives if outside your HA (not needed for minor surgery claims).

❻ *Notes* – where a continuous claim for contraceptive services is made, enter date of patient's previous acceptance by the doctor in this column. This column may also be used to enter other notes, e.g. to indicate that a patient should not be contacted without prior reference to GP.

❼ *Authorized signature* – please ensure that the declaration is read before signing.

❽ *Practice stamp*.

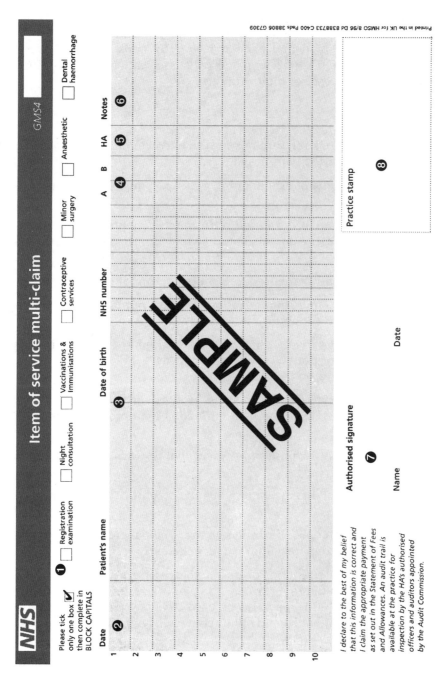

Figure 9.6 Item of service multi-claim – Form GMS4.

GMS/E: Claims summary (Figure 9.7)

Use of this envelope is optional for the summarizing and submission of claims to HA.

Adult vaccination claims (FP73 (MULTI))

This form provides for up to 20 adult vaccination claims at a time. It should not be used for patients aged 16 years or under. Please ensure the reason vaccination is given is entered on the form (Figure 9.8).

Vaccination claims (FP73)

This form should be used for vaccination claims for non-targeted children (i.e. 5–16 years) (Figure 9.9).

Notification of immunizations for targeted children (five years and under) (FP73/3/GP and FP73/2/GP)

Form FP73/3/GP (primary immunizations)

This form is in four parts. The top sheet records the child's personal details and the first dose of immunization and, once completed, should be sent to the health authority – the remaining parts are retained to record the second and third doses. The second sheet retains the details from the first sheet and provides space for the second dose details. Once completed, this sheet should be sent to the health authority. The third sheet retains details from the first two sheets and provides space for the third dose to be recorded and it should then be passed on as before. The remaining sheet (card) is the file copy and is for retention by the GP for inclusion in his/her files (Figure 9.10).

Form FP73/2/GP (MMR, boosters and ad hoc)

This form is in two parts. Once completed the top sheet should be passed on to the health authority – the remaining sheet is the file copy and can be used by the GP for his/her records (Figure 9.11).

NHS   **Claims summary**   *GMS/E*

Please list enclosures of claims and registrations.
All claims need NHS number and date of birth to speed payment.

Item of service multi-claims summary   Number of claims   HA only

Item of service multi-claims summary			Number of claims	HA only
Registration medical examination				
Night visit				
Vaccinations & Immunisations		A		
		B		
Contraceptive services	Non-IUD	A		
	IUD	B		
Minor surgery (number of sessions not procedures)				
Anaesthetic				
Dental haemorrhage				

SAMPLE

I am also enclosing   Number of forms   HA only

I am also enclosing	Number of forms	HA only
Family doctor services registration/		
Maternity medical services claim/s		
Temporary services claim/s		

Date of submission

In case of query contact

Practice stamp

Printed in the UK for HMSO – Dd. 8388395, 750,000 5/96

Figure 9.7   Claims summary – Form GMS/E.

Forms, fees and finances in general practice   181

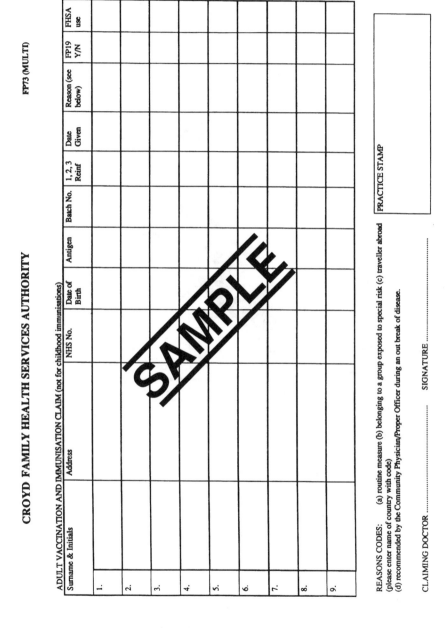

Figure 9.8   Adult vaccination claims – FP73 (MULTI).

VACCINATION AND IMMUNISATION ATTENDANCE AT:					FP 73 (Revised 12/88)				
					CLINIC/SURGERY:				
SURNAME:					SEX: MALE/FEMALE				
FORENAMES:					D.O.B.:				
ADDRESS:					POST CODE:				
SCHOOL:			NHS NO.:		CHILD HEALTH NO.:				
GENERAL PRACTITIONER'S SURNAME AND INITIALS:									
HEALTH VISITOR'S CASE LIST NO.:			(OR HV'S NAME:						)

I consent to my child receiving the following immunisations:

Poliomyelitis	Diphtheria	Tetanus	Whooping Cough	Measles	Mumps	Rubella
☐	☐	☐	☐	☐	☐	☐

Signature of Parent of Guardian .... Date ....

TO BE COMPLETED BY PERSON ADMINISTERING IMMUNISATION:

Primary Courses		BATCH NO.	DOSE	DATE	NAME	DESIG.	STAFF ID NO.
First Dose	Diphtheria						
	Tetanus						
	Pertussis						
	Poliomyelitis						
Others (please specify) 1.							
2.							
Second Dose	Diphtheria						
	Tetanus						
	Pertussis						
	Poliomyelitis						
Others (please specify) 1.							
2.							
Third Dose	Diphtheria						
	Tetanus						
	Pertussis						
	Poliomyelitis						
Others (specify)							
	Measles						
	Mumps						
	Rubella						
Boosters	Diphtheria						
	Tetanus						
	Polio						
Others (please specify) 1.							
2.							

Date and Result of any test of Immunity for Rubella:

Comments:

TO BE COMPLETED BY GENERAL PRACTITIONER CLAIMING PAYMENT

Vaccinated as ☐ (a) A routine Measure

☐ (b) Belonging to a group exposed to special risk

(Please tick) ☐ (c) A traveller to .... (Name of Country)

☐ (d) Recommended by the Proper Officer during an outbreak of disease

Name and address of General Practitioner (BLOCK CAPITALS OR STAMP)

I certify that the patient has been vaccinated as indicated above and I claim the appropriate fees.

Date .... Signature of Doctor ....

No:

Signature of Assistant or Locum on behalf of Doctor ....

PLEASE SUBMIT THIS FORM TO THE IMMUNISATION DEPARTMENT, 12-18 LENNARD ROAD, AS SOON AS EACH DOSE IS GIVEN. PLEASE DO NOT WAIT FOR COMPLETION OF A COURSE.

Figure 9.9   Vaccination claims – FP73.

CROYD COMMUNITY HEALTH/GP — IMMUNISATION RECORD

Surname	Forenames	Sex	DOB	CHS No.
		M/F		

Address	Surgery/Clinic/Home/School

GP Name & Initials	HV Name	HV (CHS) No.	NHS No.

FOR PRIMARY IMMUNISATIONS ONLY

CONSENT BY PERSON WITH PARENTAL RESPONSIBILITY:

Diphtheria	☐	Whooping Cough	☐
Tetanus	☐	Hib	☐
Poliomyelitis	☐		

I consent to my child receiving these immunisations

Signed: .... Date: ....

1ST DOSE - DELETE ANTIGEN(S) NOT GIVEN.   DETAILS OF 1ST AND SUBSEQUENT DOSES MUST BE SHOWN ON SUBSEQUENT COPIES

ANTIGEN	BATCH No.	DATE	NAME	STAFF ID OR DESIGNATION
1	Dip/Tet/Pert			
1	Oral Polio			
1	Hib			

FP/73/3/GP
(revised 2/92)

Figure 9.10   Notification of immunizations for targeted children – FP73/3/GP.

Post payment verification

In place of most pre-payment checking, HAs will now pay the claims submitted by practices and undertake post payment verification of claims. This process should not be seen as mistrust of practices but as an opportunity to provide practices with greater freedom whilst maintaining probity and ensuring that HAs fulfil the obligation with public money. Post payment verification can be carried out both at the practice and at the HA.

HAs will use management information systems to enable them to undertake comparative analysis of claims against local and national averages. Claims may be investigated by routinely contacting patients and at least once every three years practices will be visited by a team from the HA for an onsite verification of claims.

Practices should maintain up-to-date records in support of claims and must make these records available as necessary to the verification teams. HA staff will need access to practice-held records to help with the verification of claims and, as this may include relevant entries in clinical records, it is important to ensure that confidentiality is maintained at all times.

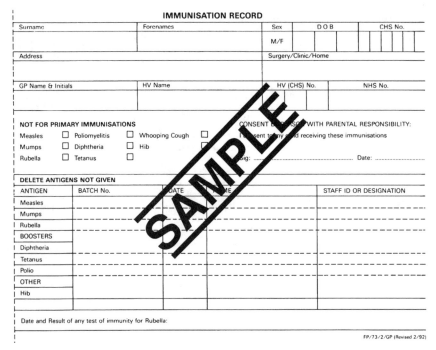

Figure 9.11   Notification of immunizations of targeted children – FP73/2/GP.

How can practices prepare for verification visits?

- The health authority will normally contact the practice in advice to arrange a mutually suitable time for the visit.

- Normally the visit will be undertaken by two HA staff.

- Ensure **now** that you have adequate systems and records in place in support of claims, that are readily available for inspection. The HA will not impose systems on you, but you may wish to network with other local practices to share good practice in record keeping. A good audit trail will have source documents, dated and flagged with identity of who created or updated them, stored in a way that can be readily accessed, and clearly traceable to claims.

- Ensure that your records are up-to-date.

- Ensure that you always obtain signatures where these are needed, or that you note clearly why they are not available.

- Ensure that staff preparing claims are competent in their preparation and are aware of the appropriate regulations.

- Note that the practice records accompanying the new forms are not adequate evidence to support claims.

- Exploit your computer systems whenever possible to assist with the organization of information.

- Test your systems regularly by tacking through random claims to see that the evidence is all available.

- HA staff will normally be seeking 100% verification. Ensure that you seek the same with your own checks.

- HA staff may be sampling 20 claims per claim type, and the visit may last approximately half a day per practice. A partner, or more likely the practice manager, should be available to assist with the process.

- Ensure that archived data is readily available. The sampled claims may stretch over a number of years.

- HA staff will discuss any findings with you before they leave. After the visit you will be sent a written report. If there are anomalies you may be invited to comment on the report before it is considered for action within the authority.

- Be prepared to raise any queries with HA staff. Look on this visit as an opportunity to improve working procedures and relationships.

Anomalies in claims would probably be picked up by methods other than practice visits under most circumstances, so you should have been given an opportunity to sort these out. The visit is part of a verification process, not a check or formal audit. If for any reason you have concerns about a proposed visit, you should contact your local medical committee if you cannot resolve these concerns with the HA.

The following protocol is typical of the procedure adopted by health authorities when carrying out a post payment verification visit.

POST PAYMENT VERIFICATION VISIT

1 **Post payment verification visit objectives**

The general objective of PPV visits is so that the health authority can gain assurance that claims submitted by practices are proper and in accordance with the Statement of Fees and Allowances (SFA). The visit is not exclusively looking for possible over-claims but also possible under-claims by practices. Specifically, the objectives are as follows:

- to gain assurance that GPs have provided the service to their patient for which claims for payment have been submitted to the health authority

- to assess whether claims made are in compliance with the SFA

- to disseminate good practice and to agree actions in respect of problem areas encountered

- to give the practice the opportunity to demonstrate their working practices and to raise any particular problems with which the PPV team could help.

2   Composition of PPV visit

Each practice visit will comprise two elements:

- an assessment of the control environment – to understand the systems and procedures within the practice for submitting each type of claim. This assessment will help give assurance that claims are submitted properly and in accordance with the SFA

- a sample of claims paid will then be traced back to the underlying records to prove their validity.

3   PPV visit method

3.1   Practice briefing

An introductory briefing will take place at the start of the visit to discuss the format of the visit, visit and practice roles and the likely timescales expected for the visit.

3.2   Assessment of systems and procedures

An assessment of systems and procedures may highlight areas for improvement in controls over processing of claims or in how to improve the efficiency in the way claims are processed, for example by reducing paperwork.

The objective of this assessment is to gain assurance that:

- there are adequate procedures for recording services provided by the practice to patients

- there is a satisfactory understanding and application of the provisions set out in the SFA in respect of each claim type

- systems exist to prevent errors and omissions, as far as possible, in the claims submitted.

Discussions with practice staff will take place to establish the systems and procedures currently being used within the practice.

3.3 Items of service validation

3.3.1 Objective

The objective of this exercise is to ensure that all claims are valid, i.e. they are in respect of treatment which took place. This is done by checking to see that each claim is supported by an appropriate entry in the practice records to prove that the patient was seen and received the treatment as claimed.

3.3.2 Sample selection

A random sample of claims received and paid by the health authority will be selected prior to attendance at the practice. The random sample will be taken from a range of claims which are normally submitted.

The sample size will be based on the list size of the practice in comparison with the average practice list size in the HA. The average list size per GP in most areas is 200, for which the sample size will be a total of 100 claims. The sample will be adjusted to reflect the list size of the practice being visited.

The claims selected will be validated against practice records.

3.3.3 Access to medical records

Access to patient medical records by the Health Authority Visit Team will be restricted to vouching the specific medical entry in order to support the practice claim. The team will not require access, and should not request access, to other patient medical records.

The specific medical entry may be found by the practice manager or other person nominated by the practice, and shown to the health authority team member.

Alternatively, to minimize the impact on the practice workload, the practice may prefer that the health authority staff find the relevant entries themselves. This is a matter of choice for the practice concerned and, where possible, preference should be made known to the visit team in advance of the visit.

The procedure to access medical records is similar to that used by internal and external auditors carried out at fundholding practices for the past five years.

All health authority staff are bound by their contractual obligations to maintain confidentiality at all times.

3.4 Reporting

At the completion stage of the post payment verification practice visit, the visit team will give a verbal representation of key findings of the visit. Practice verbal comments will be invited and documented.

A draft written report will be sent to practices for formal practice responses which will be incorporated into the final report. The final report will then be sent to the practice.

10

Using information technology

What's in the box? Basic terminology

HARDWARE	Physical components of the system, such as display screens, printers, keyboard, mouse, disks, etc.
SOFTWARE	A set of programmed instructions in the computer which enable it to respond to input of information, and demands to change it, store it or print it out in various forms
CPU	The CPU, or central processor unit, is the part of the system that performs arithmetic operations, and controls the storage, display, communication and manipulation of information. It is the part of the machine closest to a 'brain'
VDU	The screen used to display information held on the computer
KEYBOARD	A device like a typewriter to enter information into a computer. Many specialized systems use non-standard keyboards or make a lot of use of special function keys to save typing effort
MOUSE	A small hand-operated pointer which the user moves on a pad to move an arrow on the screen. Clicking a button on the mouse activates a number of operations without the need to type in text

PRINTER	Prints text and diagrams held on the computer onto paper. Older machines work like typewriters and are noisy and slow. Newer types work more like photocopiers or paint sprayers, and are much faster and quieter
DISK	Information cannot be permanently stored in the CPU. Usually it is stored on magnetic disk or tape. Tape is used for long-term secure storage and disk for information in constant use
FLOPPY DISK	These are disks which can be inserted into one computer and read by another. Most are 3.5 inches in diameter and contained in a rigid plastic case
HARD DISK	These are permanently stored in the CPU and are used to store information needed on a permanent basis by a single user. Hard disks can hold many hundred times the information of a floppy
WORK STATION	The work area where a computer operator works. Health and safety legislation gives details of how work stations should be designed
TERMINAL	A machine capable of entering and retrieving information from a multi-user computer system. It may be a computer in its own right or, more usually, just a keyboard and screen
NETWORK	When many people need to use the same computer system, several terminals can be linked together with cables. This, and the software needed for communication with a central CPU, is called a network
BYTE	This is the measure of information a computer can store. A byte is equivalent to a single text character, one megabyte equals one million bytes. The more bytes of memory a computer, or disk, has, the more information it can store

How a computer works

It is not necessary to understand fully how computers work in order to operate the systems in use in GP practices, clinics and hospitals. The following brief outline is given for interest.

The central processor unit uses a system of on–off switches to hold information in a memory. Each number or character is expressed as a sequence of on or off states in a group of switches which together form a *byte.* As the operator enters information into the computer it is translated into machine readable form and stored in the *random access memory* (RAM). This process is controlled by the computer's internal *operating system.* This is the raw material which is worked on by the computer's *application software,* which tells the machine how to display and manipulate the data to achieve the operator's needs and how to interpret the instructions given by the operator.

The most common types of software are *word processors* which enable users to write documents, edit and print them. Most have facilities to store lists of names and addresses and write these into one of a series of previously written standard letters. Routine correspondence can be produced far more efficiently in this way. Individual parts of a document can be edited without the need for wholesale retyping. Importantly, information stored on one computer within a system (such as a patient administration system), can be imported onto another without the need to retype it.

Databases are applications designed to hold a lot of information about a series of people or things. An individual record (a patient for instance) contains a variety of *fields* which may have general text such as name, address and details of medical conditions. The field could have a specialized or limited range of values like a postcode, date, male or female; or it could be a code obtained from a published table like diagnostic codings for different medical conditions. These codes are much easier for a computer system to analyse than free text which really needs a human brain to interpret.

Spreadsheets are especially suited to putting in order, displaying and performing calculations on mathematical data. They are commonly used to analyse treatments given to a large number of patients or to calculate and report on budgets and expenditure. A typical small spreadsheet is shown below:

PROJECTED QUARTERLY EXPENDITURE ON STAFF TRAINING				
Expenditure	First quarter	Second quarter	Third quarter	Fourth quarter
Staff time	£1287	£10 663	£7 287	£5288
Expenses	£325	£8 825	£8 350	£3000
Total	£1612	£19 488	£15 637	£8288

Computers in general practice

General practice today is such a complex organization, and it is doubtful whether management of its administration can be effectively handled without information technology (IT). A computerized practice is:

- more efficient
- in greater control of patient care
- able to generate more income.

Patient benefits through computerization

- Improved preventive care through the identification of 'at risk' groups, patient group analysis and follow-up.
- Reducing the risk of disease through immunization/vaccination.
- The early detection of disease through developmental screening, hypertensive monitoring, geriatric surveillance, etc.
- The management of established disease.
- More selective advice on smoking, drinking, etc.
- Better information on the patient services available.*

*(Source: Royal College of General Practitioners, *Computers in General Practice Guidance Notes*.)

The uses of an up-to-date patient database include:

- patient information data
- age–sex register
- logging and generation of repeat prescriptions
- logging and checking patient registration status
- checking immunization/cervical cytology status
- screening and recall
- diagnosis and morbidity data
- opportunistic screening.

A computerized appointments system overcomes the difficulties of manual appointment books, e.g. illegible handwriting, pages messy with cancellations, two people not being able to use the book at the same time, handwritten surgery lists for pulling out records, are all circumvented.

Reference had been made to using IT for written communication in Chapter 3. Secretaries and receptionists are now able to produce letters using a wordprocessing package to generate mail-merged letters, or readily produce letters to patients. Spreadsheets can be used either to collect data (for display in tables, graphs and pie charts) or to present doctor and staff rotas.

Desktop publishing software can be used to generate leaflets, posters and handouts.

Technology can save time for some tasks; in others it does not save time, but it does make it possible to produce professional looking documents, for example, practice leaflets, charts and posters.

For those who enjoy using a computer, it is essential that the computer does not become a barrier between the patient and the secretary or receptionist. Remember, it is equally rude to continue to input/extract data as it is to continue to talk to a colleague or take a telephone call without acknowledging the presence of a patient.

The major disadvantage of IT in the practice is when the system 'goes down'; the increased efficiency disappears and returning to manual systems, no matter how temporarily, results in unavoidable delays and disruption.

Age–sex register and patient information

These are basic patient data put onto the computer. Secretaries and receptionists will receive specific training in the use of their practice's information system.

The importance of inputting data accurately cannot be overstated as this information will be of vital importance to the practice's activities. Remember, too, to always input the postcode; it is a vital piece of information and should be cross-checked with the medical record in your possession.

You should be aware of the requirements of the Data Protection Act, and must respect the security and confidentiality of patient information at all times.

Registration data

This information is of immense value; it includes all information regarding registration status:

- date patient registered with the practice
- date patient was accepted on the doctor's list
- date patient was included in a GP's patient list.

It will also indicate the category and date of a patient's removal from a doctor's list, e.g., when moving out of the area, or on death.

Repeat prescriptions

A computerized system can save much of the receptionist's time by obviating the need to retrieve patient files and other manually held prescribing information. It also:

- produces a legible, printed and accurate prescription
- places a time limit on the issue of repeat prescriptions
- monitors the rate and consumption of drugs
- updates the repeat prescription record
- identifies easily patients who are on a particular medication.

Screening and recall

The ability of a computer to search rapidly on specific criteria can allow a practice to identify certain groups of patients:

- selected for information (e.g. asthmatics, hypertensives, diabetics, etc.) for health promotion banding, and who would benefit from additional care and those who are considered to be 'at risk'
- who are eligible for item-of-service claims.

The computer can also help with:

- crisis intervention
- the control of chronic diseases
- preventive medicine
- generating additional income for the practice.

Diagnoses and morbidity

A computer has the capacity and speed to extract and analyse data on any topics of particular interest to the practice, for example to analyse morbidity and treatment within the practice. The latest RCGP (Royal College of General Practitioners) coding system has been developed with a view to collecting these types of data from as many practices as possible.

Social recording

Computer systems are also capable of recording information on height/weight/smoking and alcohol habits so as to provide the health authority/health board with statistics for practices claiming health promotion banding allowances. This information is automatically included in the patients' records.

Electronic links and other developments

Information technology is rapidly advancing and over 7000 medical practices are now linked directly to health authorities across England and Wales. All health authorities are now transmitting items of service to over 3000 practices (see Table 10.1 which shows performance as at December 1996).

Electronic Links convey correspondence, such as patient test results and consultant letters, directly between the sender's and the recipient's computer systems. The electronic linkage is performed by using public and private telephone networks. The technical term used for the transfer of such data is electronic data interchange (EDI) where the sender's information is converted into a form which can be conveyed through telephone lines via a modem.

Table 10.1   League table for the implementation of registration Links.

Health authority	Total no. of computerized practices at April 1996 (baseline)	Total no. of linked practices at Dec 1996	%
Northumberland	44	48	109
Hillingdon	47	51	109
Newcastle/North Tyne	71	74	104
Barnsley	34	35	103
Kingston & Richmond	62	62	100
Dorset	97	96	99

Health authority	Total no. of computerized practices at April 1996 (baseline)	Total no. of linked practices at Dec 1996	%
Hertfordshire	120	118	98
Wirral	57	56	98
Bromley	51	50	98
West Sussex	97	95	98
South Humber	47	46	98
Bradford	89	87	98
Wakefield	39	38	97
Dyfed & Powys	73	71	97
East Sussex	130	126	97
Solihull	32	31	97
Sefton	52	50	96
Croydon	65	62	95
Surrey	148	141	95
Sandwell	63	60	95
Somerset	73	69	95
Buckinghamshire	90	85	94
Stockport	53	50	94
Avon	134	126	94
Manchester	81	76	94
North Wales	110	103	94
Northamptonshire	77	72	94
Berkshire	103	95	92
Cambridge & Huntingdon	61	56	92
Cornwall	71	65	92
Oxfordshire	82	75	91
East Riding	81	74	91
East Kent	102	93	91
North West Anglia	53	48	91
Enfield & Haringey	105	95	90
Walsall	52	47	90
Gateshead/South Tyne	57	51	89
Doncaster	45	40	89
Sunderland	52	46	88
Durham	86	76	88
Shropshire	57	50	88
Dudley	48	42	88
North Yorkshire	109	95	87
Ealing Hamms. & Houns.	124	108	87
Tees	85	74	87
Coventry	46	40	87
Calderdale	107	93	87
Camden & Islington	75	65	87
Barking Havrg. & Brentwd.	89	77	87

Health authority	Total no. of computerized practices at April 1996 (baseline)	Total no. of linked practices at Dec 1996	%
North West Lancs	73	63	86
Southampton	64	53	84
Kensington CW	70	59	84
West Kent	166	139	84
Merton, Sutton & Wdsworth	134	112	84
Bexley & Greenwich	85	71	84
St Helens & Knowsley	60	50	83
Liverpool	84	70	83
Barnet	66	55	83
West Pennine	75	62	83
Icheydd Morganwyg	75	62	83
Lincolnshire	98	81	83
Wiltshire & Bath	80	66	83
Gloucestershire	80	66	83
East London & City	128	105	82
Hereford	26	21	81
Redbridge & Walth. Forest	94	75	80
Morecambe Bay	42	33	79
East Norfolk	84	66	79
Essex	222	174	78
South Cheshire	90	70	78
Gwent	108	84	78
Leeds	114	88	77
Bury & Rochdale	74	57	77
Leicestershire	127	97	76
Bro Taf	130	99	76
North & East Devon	70	53	76
Bedfordshire	86	65	76
North & Mid Hampshire	68	51	75
Bolton & Wigan	99	74	75
South Lancashire	51	38	75
Isle of Wight	19	14	74
South & West Devon	91	66	73
Lambeth S'wark & Lsham	150	108	72
Portsmouth	71	51	72
Salford & Trafford	84	60	71
East Lancashire	99	70	71
Brent & Harrow	109	77	71
North Cumbria	47	33	70
Worcestershire	67	46	69
North Cheshire	44	30	68
Rotherham	40	27	68
Warwickshire	71	46	65

Health authority	Total no. of computerized practices at April 1996 (baseline)	Total no. of linked practices at Dec 1996	%
North Nottingham	57	36	63
Sheffield	96	60	63
Southern Derbyshire	79	48	61
Northern Derbyshire	57	34	60
Suffolk	89	51	57
Nottingham Health	103	59	57
Birmingham	208	118	57
South Staffordshire	82	45	55
Wolverhampton	47	25	53
North Staffordshire	96	50	52
Total	8355	6897	83

NB Where % figure exceeds 100% this denotes an increase in the number of computerized practices since the baseline was set in April 1996.

Advantages of electronic Links are:

• less duplication of task, e.g. patient registration

• fewer transcription errors (where data are entered once only)

• reduced paper work (form-filling)

• easier and faster access to information.

The main applications for electronic Links are:

• Links with the practice health authority for the exchange of:

  – patient registration information

  – items of service claims.

• Links with local hospitals, for the exchange of:

  – patient referral correspondence between GPs and consultants

  – laboratory test results and reports and requests from GPs.

Pathology Links are being used by some health authorities to facilitate results of tests to general medical practitioners. The main benefit of this is that individual test results, e.g. blood haemoglobin level or results of a full blood count, can be 'posted' directly into the clinical notes of patients. 'Posting' removes the need to type the results into the system, saving time

NATIONWIDE

HEALTHLINK
NETWORK
(National)

LOCAL AREA

Secure electronic 'mailboxes'
contain each Healthlink
subscriber's data

Local GP practices

GPs

Local HA

HAs

Figure 10.1   The HA/GP Links project: making the connections.

and possible data entry errors. Doctors will be able to select which results they wish to see, e.g. abnormal results highlighted by the laboratory will be displayed on the screen.

As well as being 'posted' into the notes, results may also be marked 'for action' by practice staff, e.g. a re-test or an appointment with the GP may be necessary.

As part of the *Patients not Paper* initiative, the NHS Executive has set up a project called GP Provider Links ('Trailblazers') which is pioneering standard communication links between practices and hospitals.

Computers in hospitals

Computerization of records in a hospital works well because there is a great deal of information to be stored and consulted, information is required by a variety of people at different times and in different locations, much of the information needs to be sorted or changed and complex analysis of data is needed.

This is not because computers are 'clever'. They are not, they have no real intelligence or ability to think of solutions. However computers can process vast amounts of data at incredible speed with virtually no errors. A 'computer error' is almost always a human operator doing the wrong thing or the computer's programmer setting it up wrongly in the first place.

The main systems used in hospitals are the patient administration system (PAS), word processing, and record storage in pathology, X-ray and pharmacy. Other major systems are used in finance and personnel departments, estates management and supplies, and are being introduced into nursing and theatre management.

Patient administration systems (PAS)

The potential of computers has long been exploited in hospitals in the area of patient administration. There are many versions used by different hospitals, but all have the following component parts:

PATIENT INDEX	Records of the personal details of every patient
ADMISSIONS, DISCHARGES AND TRANSFERS	A record of each patient's history of time spent in the hospital as an inpatient or outpatient, with particular consultants or in a particular department
WAITING LISTS	Names and dates of referral of all patients waiting for inpatient and/or outpatient treatment
OUTPATIENTS	A system to manage appointments and correspondence associated with outpatient clinics
GP INDEX	A list of the names and addresses of all the local GPs

Nursing management systems

Increasingly, hospitals are being equipped with computer systems to help nurses plan and keep track of the nursing care of patients. Patients' details are retrieved from PAS and a detailed plan of their expected care is prepared. Care given is recorded onto the system to help co-ordinate the work of the team. Patient dependency levels can be predicted from the care plans and nurse rosters are drawn up to match needs.

Order communication systems

In most hospitals, ordering portering services, pathology tests, supplies of materials or repairs to buildings or equipment must be done by telephone or by completing a form, often with multiple copies and posting it to the relevant department. This can take a long time and involve much duplication of effort. An order communications (or 'order-comms') system allows ordering departments to send requests for services directly to the department, and receive confirmation of orders or the results of tests directly.

Hospital information support system (HISS)

The trend among hospitals with well established computer systems is to integrate them into one powerful scheme called a hospital information support system (HISS). Such a system allows every department's computer system to talk to those of other departments, to transfer information and to generate reports.

Getting the best from the computer

The importance of inputting data accurately cannot be overstated, as this information is to be used by health care professionals in treating and caring for patients, for statistical analysis and planning, for budgeting, for contract monitoring and invoicing for services. Information held on the computer must be regularly cross-checked with that held on medical records, and amended as necessary. Incorrect information about a patient can lead to important letters or test results going astray.

Frequent problems which arise in hospitals are caused by out-of-date addresses, either because the patient has moved house or changed GP or both. Other problems arise from incomplete details, or temporary addresses entered as permanent, for example when a person is taken ill when visiting relatives. Errors in this information can be very costly to the hospital, since if the bill is sent to the wrong health authority or GP fund-holder they are unlikely to pay.

The barrier created by the computer

Computer systems usually require patient information to be input in a specific sequence which may not be the same as that which the patient wants to give. Sometimes the computer is slow to respond if a lot of people are using it. Receptionist staff frequently have to deal with a patient on the phone, another in person and call up details onto their screen, all at the same time. Both patient and receptionist start to feel that they are the servant of the computer, rather than the other way round.

To overcome these difficulties it is important to explain to the patient what is happening (especially when on the telephone) and develop a sequence of questions which gives the information you need in the correct order. This often requires a good deal of practice and discussion with col-leagues before it works really well.

Maintaining security

There are four main risks to be guarded against when using computer systems:

- unauthorized access to information held on computer

- loss of information due to mechanical failure

- theft of machinery

- spoiling of information by computer viruses.

Preventing unauthorized access

Information about people held on computer is governed by the Data Protection Act. It should only be used for the purpose for which it was col-lected and should not be revealed to unauthorized people. Where pass-word systems exist, these must be used. Passwords should never be shared or revealed to others. Computer screens should face away from public areas. Terminals should not be left unattended showing data or even 'logged in' to a system, since anyone may then gain access.

Backing up – keeping spare copies of information

If information has been stored on a computer's hard disk and it is lost due to mechanical failure or theft a great deal of work will be needed to replace it. It is extremely important to keep copies on a separate storage device. Taking such copies is known as backing up and should be done daily. Staff using a multi-user system may find that it is done centrally by a system manager. Each night the latest data is copied onto large tape recorders.

Personal computers should be backed up either to a central back up store via a hospital network, or to removable floppy disks, or specially designed tape records (called tape streamers). Locally made back up copies should be stored away from the computer in case of theft or fire.

Guarding against theft

Backing up is also important in case a computer is stolen. Such thefts are becoming increasingly common from hospitals and health care premises. Premises should be secure and kept locked. Machinery should be indelibly marked and preferably fastened to the desktop and alarmed with one of a variety of proprietary products. Computers should be housed away from public view wherever possible, e.g. away from windows without blinds.

Computer viruses

These are small programs designed to damage data held on computer. They are transferred from one machine to another when other files are copied, perhaps from floppy disk or by electronic connection. To guard against this, material should never be copied from a disk which has not been checked for viruses, nor should games and other such programs be copied onto work machines. Computer equipment and disks should be routinely checked for the presence of virus programs.

Illegal use of software

Commercial computer programs are protected by copyright. Generally a program can only be used on one computer unless a site licence has been purchased. The penalties for using programs which are not licensed are extremely high.

Computers and the law

Where medical records are stored on computer it is a requirement that computer-held material is at least as confidential as a paper record. Special care must be taken with computerized information, since it is possible to write programs which allow different people different levels of access. For example, it is possible to give a doctor access via the computer to all the information held, whereas the clerk may only see certain material. Some staff will be allowed to change information, others will have 'read only' access.

The Data Protection Act 1984 (see Chapter 4)

Organizations which record information relating to identifiable living individuals on computer must ensure that they comply with the provisions of the Data Protection Act. This Act applies to England, Wales, Scotland and Northern Ireland.

The Data Protection Act is based on eight principles and is designed to ensure that information relating to an individual is obtained fairly, is kept up to date and is stored securely. The individual whose data are stored has rights of access enabling him or her to check the accuracy of the information. The data protection registrar and the courts are empowered to require correction of inaccurate material if it is not undertaken voluntarily by the data user.

New developments

The aim of the NHS information strategy is to ensure that data can move securely throughout the NHS network. For example:

- requirements for accreditation are intended to develop a convergence of system standards, thus simplifying the task of enabling computer systems to communicate with each other

- new NHS numbers will avoid the problems of number duplication and simplify patient confidentiality with EDI

- an NHS network will comprise a national network linking all health authorities and central registries, to which will be linked local networks to include laboratories, hospitals and GP surgeries.

Looking forward: the computer-based patient record

The electronic patient record in the UK

In January 1994, the Information Management Group of the NHS Executive organized a three year project to enable health care professionals in acute hospitals to give better care to patients through the use of the electronic patient records systems. The outcome of the research is intended to feed into the development of clinical systems which will be available at some point in the future. A major objective is to improve patient care through electronic patient record systems and to explore the value to clinicians of integrated electronic patient record systems. The following reasons for developing the computerized patient record were outlined in *Aspects of the Computer-based Patient Record* (1992):

- the uses of and demand for patient data are increasing

- the increasing complexity of treatments and an increasing elderly population

- a mobile population which needs to be tracked

- to improve quality and manage costs.

Electronic paper records (EPR) can include everything that is currently held in the paper record, and may contain text, sound and images, e.g. X-rays. The information contained in the EPR can be sorted, summarized or reported upon and put to a number of uses.

Patient administration systems used in hospitals contain mostly administrative details but there are also the much larger hospital information support systems (HISS). These contain many patient-based details, including order communications and incorporated test results (see p. 201).

Another type of electronic record is known as the 'smart card' – similar to the plastic credit card – which has information recorded on an integrated circuit chip. These cards contain patient's identification details, blood groups, allergies, GP and a summary of the medical record. The benefits of smart cards are that they are portable and can be held by patients.

There are no examples in the UK as yet of a fully integrated EPR system although some hospitals are working towards fully computerized records.

The new NHS number

The key to effective sharing of information about patients is the ability to identify a person in a way which is common throughout the NHS. The use of a common single identifier will be the key to the exchange of clinical and administrative information between systems and health care workers. The existing NHS number is not suitable for computerized information systems and will in due course be replaced.

The 'paperless' practice

It has been suggested that medical practices go 'paperless'. Indeed, many practices would like to take advantage of computerized record keeping and electronic transfer of data as this would lead to a reduction in practice workload and ensure legibility and uniformity of medical records. Unfortunately current systems are not designed to produce a literary patient record but they do provide an excellent record of drug history and details of current treatment.

The GP's terms of service does not recognize computer records and it is therefore possible that a paperless practice could be found in breach of its terms of service. Although some practices do keep computerized records, they maintain paper records at the same time. No doubt in the future, legitimate computerized medical records will be possible but only when a suitable system is developed through which full medical records can be transferred electronicallly between different areas of the health service.

NHS Direct

An innovation proposed in *The New NHS: modern and dependable*, NHS Direct will offer people immediate access to advice and information in their own homes, as an alternative to either visiting the surgery or calling out their medical practitioner in situations which are not genuine emergencies. It will offer patients the opportunity to take control in protecting their own health and that of their families while, at the same time, taking some pressure off GPs and A&E departments.

GP Links to the NHSnet

Patients in the community will benefit through the connection of every GP surgery and hospital to the NHSnet, e.g. quicker results, on-line specialist advice and ease of appointments. Demonstration sites are planned and it is anticipated these services will be available across the country by 2002.

11

Medical terminology and clinical aspects

Introduction

Medical secretaries and receptionists, with their unique skills of dealing with doctors, other professionals and patients, with tact and courtesy, will find that a knowledge of medical terminology will help them to carry out their duties in a more effective and efficient manner. Very often the words and phrases used by medical professionals are long, difficult and frequently appear to be obscure.

Medical terminology is based upon root words derived from Greek and Latin. To these roots may be added syllabuses that modify the meaning of the root word. An addition made to the front of a root is known as a *prefix;* an addition at the end is a *suffix*. Over the years this principle has been modified in such a way that it can be applied to modern medical techniques. For example, the root 'gaster' means 'stomach'. By adding the suffix 'itis' the word is modified to mean 'inflammation of the stomach'; or by the addition of 'oscopy' we have gastroscopy, which means in this modified form 'visual inspection of the stomach' (by means of a gastroscope).

It is not intended to go into a detailed explanation of medical terminology, but to point out that a limited knowledge of some root words, prefixes and suffixes will give a wider understanding of the medical vocabulary. Appendix 4 lists some of the most commonly used root words, prefixes and suffixes.

Medical abbreviations are also frequently used by professionals in health care, and a knowledge of these will also be of value. (See Appendix 4.)

Pathology and X-ray examinations

Medical secretaries and receptionists will find that doctors refer patients for pathological and other investigations and tests. An awareness of the most commonly used tests will not only contribute to the effectiveness of their day-to-day work, but will also make their job more interesting and fulfilling. (See Appendix 4.)

Prescribing and drugs

The supply, distribution and storage of drugs are controlled by a series of Acts of Parliament, designed to control their sale and to reduce their danger to life from sale by unqualified persons.

Secretaries and receptionists will find that a knowledge of the drugs most frequently used by the medical practice or hospital consultant will be of value in their day-to-day work.

Receptionists in general practice have greater direct involvement with repeat prescribing for their patients and will often have to deal with queries. However, the receptionist must have clear instructions and never be placed in the position of making medical decisions.

Components of a prescription

The following information must be included on every prescription issued by the doctor, whether it be an NHS or a private prescription. Without this information it is not possible for the pharmacist to dispense the drugs. Sometimes it could be that the writing on the prescription is illegible, but this is not so common now that repeat prescriptions in general practice are computer-generated.

Drug name

This may be written in the generic or approved name of the drug, or its trade, or proprietary name (see also page 212). For example:

- salbutamol (generic)
- Ventolin (proprietary).

Form of prescribed drug

This refers to whether capsules, tablets, syrup, injection, ointment, etc. are required.

Strength

Many drugs are available in more than one strength, which must be specified.

Directions

Directions to the patient regarding dosage of the medicine should be included. The *British National Formulary* recommends that directions should preferably be in English. Some doctors still use Latin abbreviations. (See Appendix 4.)

Amount or quantity

A box on the prescription form can be completed to indicate the number of days treatment is to continue. If this is not used, the quantity to be dispensed should be included.

Problems from prescriptions

Medical receptionists and secretaries should be aware that problems can be caused by:

- missing information, e.g. strength of drug, missing form or type of drug, missing dose
- incorrect or inaccurate information, e.g. incorrect name of drug (similar drug names can cause problems – *chlorpropamide* which is used for diabetics and *chlorpromazine*, a tranquillizer)
- incorrect strength or incorrect dose
- amounts of medicine prescribed (patients often complain that they have run out of one medicine and still have some others left. Remember, medicines come in different pack sizes – some in 28s some in 30s, etc.).

Controlled drugs

The relevant legislation concerning controlled drugs is the Misuse of Drugs Regulations 1985 and subsequent amendments.

For controlled drugs there are rules for :

- who can possess and supply

- record keeping

- storage

- prescription writing.

Records

Secretaries and receptionists should understand that it is the doctor's duty to maintain a register, in an approved form, of the quantity of all controlled drugs obtained and supplied, including any administered personally, including names and addresses.

Storage

All controlled drugs in the custody of a doctor must be kept in a locked cupboard that can only be opened by the doctor or with his/her authority.

It is the doctor's responsibility to ensure the controlled drugs cupboard is locked and the keys put safely away. The medical secretary or receptionist should make sure that this has been done.

Prescribing controlled drugs

Special rules apply to prescribing controlled drugs. A prescription for a controlled drug must:

- be written in ink, or otherwise so as to be indelible; it must be signed and dated by the person issuing it with his/her usual signature

- be written by the person issuing it in their own handwriting

- specify the name and address of the person for whom it is intended

- specify the strength of the preparation, the dose to be taken and the quantity of the preparation in both words and figures.

An exception to these rules is for phenobarbitone – receptionists can write these prescriptions, but the quantity must be written in both words and figures.

Repeat prescribing

The doctor is responsible for issuing the initial prescription to the patient, and explaining what the preparation is and what it is intended to do, etc. The patient does not always remember and will often discuss any problems with the receptionist or secretary.

Some patients are on regular drug regimes and are able to request repeat prescriptions without seeing the doctor every time they run out of their medication.

In general practice, receptionists play a vital role in the repeat prescription procedure of the practice:

- They receive the requests from patients for a repeat of their medication.

- They will either prepare a further prescription for the doctor's signature, or generate a repeat prescription on the practice computer to be signed by the doctor.

- A record should be kept either on the computer or in the patient's medical record (or both) of repeat prescribing.

- They will explain to the patient how to make the best use of the repeat prescription service offered by the practice, for example, the procedures and system used – the use of cards, computer print-out, or telephone requests for repeat prescriptions.

The repeat prescription system used by the medical practice is designed not only to make better use of the doctor's time, but to suit the patient's needs. Every practice has its own system to ensure that patients get their prescriptions on a regular basis.

Computer-generated prescriptions

Many practices now have a computer which will generate repeat prescriptions, instead of receptionists laboriously writing them out. Although computer-generated prescriptions are time saving, secretaries and receptionists must remember that computers are only efficient if the correct information has been entered in the first instance. Therefore, when entering details of patients' medication into the computer, always check that all the information is there, for example, the right drug, its strength, the correct dose and quantity have been entered.

Sources of information

Doctors receive a great deal of information which is designed to help them in prescribing for their patients. Medical secretaries and receptionists will, no doubt, have access to the following useful sources of information:

- *British National Formulary (BNF)*
- *Monthly Index of Medical Specialities (MIMS).*

The BNF, published twice yearly, is an official reliable source of accurate information on prescribing. MIMS is sent to doctors each month. It is a good, 'user-friendly' information source, but printing errors may occasionally occur. Both publications provide details of constituents, manufacturers, packaging, net costs, etc. of every medicine that can be prescribed.

Branded or generic

Every drug that a doctor prescribes will fall into one of two categories:

- branded
- generic.

The term 'branded' refers to the proprietary name of a drug given by a manufacturer, whilst, 'generic' means that the name is a general one which describes the pharmacological product. Both the *BNF* and *MIMS* give cross-referenced information on generic and brand-named products.

Practice prescribing policies

Prescription analysis and cost (PACT)

Secretaries and receptionists in general practice will be aware that their practice prescribing policy reflects, to a certain extent, national and local guidelines.

The Prescription Pricing Authority (PPA) sends a statement each quarter giving information on what individual doctors, and the whole practice is prescribing, how much is being spent on drugs, and how they compare locally and nationally with other doctors and practices. Health authorities indicate a target cost for each practice to aim for, which is designed to encourage effective prescribing procedures.

Practice formularies

There are many medicines and preparations available on prescription, a number of which are the same generic drug with a different proprietary name. Practices are reducing the number of drugs they prescribe and where appropriate, yet in the patients' best interests, will try to achieve the national approach.

The community pharmacist

Pharmacists, in common with general practitioners, have a contract with the NHS, which clearly states their terms of service. This contract, together with the requirements of the Medicines Act, provides the framework in which pharmacists work.

The pharmacist is a professional person who will, from time to time telephone a medical practice to speak to a doctor, or member of the team. This may be to query a prescription item or the frequency of its repeat. The receptionist or secretary should always immediately connect the pharmacist to the doctor, being aware that they are acting in accordance with legal and professional responsibility.

Many community pharmacists keep computerized records of medicines dispensed to patients, and are thus readily aware of potential problems.

12

Primary health care services and social services

Introduction

The government's policy in recent years has been to transfer care from the secondary to the primary sector, i.e. from hospitals or other institutions (such as long-term inpatient psychiatric care), to the patients being at home and supported there by relevant services.

These policies are embodied in the Health of the Nation documents which set out health targets for the nation. Within local settings, for example in Wales, health authorities/health boards have set out local strategies for health aligned with the Health of the Nation strategy, but breaking it down into achievable aims and objectives at the local level. The Community Care Act supplements the Health of the Nation strategy by providing a structure to manage the patients in their homes.

The Community Care Act gives patients (or clients) an active part in deciding what care they receive, compared to the previous situation where the health authority and social services provided a range of services and the patient received the service deemed most appropriate by doctors, nurses or social workers.

Care in the community includes both community nursing services and social services. As each patient is referred to the community nursing services (from a hospital, a general practitioner or by self referral) an assessment is carried out with the patient, and their relatives if they wish, in the home. A nursing care plan is agreed which is tailored to meet the needs of the patient. Typical services provided by community nurses would include giving injections, e.g. insulin to housebound diabetics, palliative care to patients who are dying, dressings and removal of stitches after surgery. Patients do not make any personal contribution to the cost of their care, i.e. the service is free.

With social services, a care plan is agreed between the patient and the social worker. However, the patient's financial situation is also taken into account to work out the patient's contribution towards cost. (Patients have made a contribution towards social services received for some time and no one goes without a service they need simply because they cannot afford it.) Social services provide for children and families, the elderly, patients with mental illness, learning difficulties, permanent disabilities and alcohol problems. To supplement care given by families, friends and neighbours, help may come from:

- social workers, home carers, meals on wheels
- sheltered housing, day centres, residential homes, nursing homes
- wardens and housing officers
- voluntary groups, visitors and churches.

Apart from meals on wheels which delivers a hot cooked meal to the patient's home, luncheon clubs encourage patients to socialize, carer support groups encourage family members and friends to share their experiences and support one another, and information services help patients and families to know what is available to them. Simple practical help, such as assistance with bathing, light housework, or preparing a meal is now provided by home carers who are specially trained to do this work.

Further information about community nursing or social services provided in any particular area of the country will be available from local offices who publish leaflets outlining what they provide, to whom and how to access the services.

The limit on funds for health and social care results in decisions being made about what service or care is received dependent on money available. This concept is very difficult for a nation that has come to depend on a free health service available to all at the point of need. The reality of the situation is that the Government does not have a bottomless purse, so the responsibility for deciding who receives what care is being transferred to those who deal with the patients – doctors, health and social care workers. Therefore the role of health professionals is changing from 'helping people' and responding to need, to include assessment and management, and offsetting need against available funds.

Dentists, opticians and pharmacists, like general practitioners, are contracted to the health authorities to provide their services. They are also greatly affected by the changes to the funding and structure of the health service. Fewer dental and optical services are available to patients on the

NHS so their NHS income has dropped. To remain viable they charge patients for services and sell related products, or become entirely private practice. Pharmacists' income is directly related to the value of prescriptions dispensed. Doctors are reducing their prescription bills to meet their indicative prescribing budgets and so pharmacists' income is also dropping. They supplement their income by selling more 'over the counter' and associated products and some independent local chemists are being taken over by larger chains.

Fundholding and trust status

General practitioners have been offered the opportunity to become fundholders, which allows them to contract with hospitals for investigations (X-rays, blood tests, etc.) and some inpatient and outpatient referrals. Emergency admissions, children, maternity, the elderly and some specialities (e.g. renal dialysis) are not included in the fundholding budgets at this time. There are also budgets for prescribing, staff and fund management. The administration of the funds (or budgets) is a paper exercise since the practices do not actually receive the money. They raise invoices for patient services and authorize payment to the trust hospitals via the health authority when notification of the care given to each patient is returned to the surgery. Trust hospitals are those which choose to manage their own budgets; they apply for and attain trust status, so that they can contract to provide specific services to general practice.

Where a practice negotiates contracts including clauses, for example where their patients will be seen within six weeks of referral and admitted with a further four weeks, it becomes clear that patients of fundholding practices are seen more quickly. The government has therefore laid down conditions to ensure that patients of non-fundholding practices do not have to be on a waiting list longer than one year. This is a considerable improvement on waiting lists where, for a few specialities in some areas of the country, about seven years ago a wait of well over two years was not unknown.

Trust status has also been given to ambulance services. Their whole range of services from transporting patients to hospital outpatient clinics, emergency admissions, doctors' answering service, paging, community alarms and nursing answering service are now managed against budgets with built-in standards of achievement, e.g. for patients being transported to a particular clinic, they will be picked up and returned within a specific time of their appointment so that they are not kept waiting around the hospital for hours on end.

GP commissioning: what is it?

GP commissioning is a broad concept and may be considered as a different way to engage in the planning, monitoring and procurement of care. In some ways, it is an alternative to fundholding, since fundholding is essentially about GP purchasing but on the other hand, some fundholders are in fact members of GP commissioning groups.

It is perhaps helpful to consider all GPs as commissioners, i.e. they all commission care for individual patients via the consultation process. Some GPs join with local colleagues and their health authority to form commissioning groups, whereas others purchase care directly for their patients via fundholding.

At its simplest, a group of GPs advises their health authority on the commissioning of local health care. The GPs may be local medical committee (LMC) members, who form small commissioning subcommittees, or a group of neighbouring practices who wish to have a say in how the health authority acts on their behalf.

Total purchasing

Despite the controversy surrounding the introduction of GP fundholding, it has proved to be a successful innovation. The range of services covered by fundholding practices has gradually increased since its outset but emergency admissions, for example, continued to be purchased by health authorities, while the majority of outpatient care and elective surgery was purchased by fundholders. Fundholders were not involved in strategic purchasing.

A mixture of fundholding models has evolved enabling GPs to influence purchasing decisions. Since April 1996, there have been three types of fundholding:

- total purchasing for GPs who buy all services for their patients, including emergency admissions

- standard fundholding enabling practices to purchase an enhanced range of services

- community fundholding for practices with 3000 patients or more, covering drugs, staff and community services.

Total fundholders develop local agreement with their health authority, whose budget for services outside fundholding they share. Most total purchasing groups of GPs from different practices have very different ways of working and using resources but as they come together to share a budget and develop a strategy they need to work closely together. Conventional fundholding continues alongside total purchasing with the individual practice fundholding budget top-sliced from the group's total fund and run individually by each practice.

The health authority sets up systems to monitor the total purchasing group and ensure it works to its budget and delivers agreed national and local targets. Trusts need to make adjustments for total purchases although many acute trusts price emergencies at a level which fundholders are unlikely to accept. One of the attractions of total purchasing is that if GPs reduce the lengths of stay in hospital, they bring resources out of the hospital to support patients in the community.

Total purchasing like locality purchasing is concerned with the development of primary care-led purchasing by involving GPs in the local development of health services and giving them incentives to improve not only their services to patients, but the services of other health care workers.

GP multifunds

A GP multifund is a collection of practices who have agreed to pool part of their fundholding management allowance to facilitate a central administration system for fundholding purposes within their practices. The way in which this takes place varies from multifund to multifund but they all share and benefit from economy, shared information and strength in numbers. An effective communication network including all members of the primary health care team for maintaining trust between practices is an essential ingredient for a successful multifund.

The New NHS: modern, dependable

Phasing out of fundholding

As part of its 10 year plan for an improved NHS for the 21st century, the Government's White Paper announced the end of fundholding and the internal market (see Chapter 1). While retaining the innovative nature of fundholding, the intention is to make the best features of the scheme available to the *whole* population and to break down the barriers between services. There will be no further entrance into the GP fundholding scheme.

Primary care groups

Primary care groups (PCGs) comprising all GPs in an area together with community nurses will take responsibility for commissioning services for the local community. Through commissioning services and better co-ordination of primary and community services they will work together to improve the health of local people. They will build upon the range of commissioning models that already exist.

Primary care groups will be representative of all the GP practices in the group and as such will have a governing body which includes GPs and community nursing and social services representatives drawn from the local area. A typical PCG will serve a population of around 100 000 but the size is flexible and will be determined by local circumstances. Primary care groups will mean fewer commissioners with increased powers and more freedom to make decisions about how they apply their resources in line with the health improvement programme (see Chapter 1).

Most commissioning groups will hold a single unified budget covering cash-limited medical services, hospital services and prescribing. Therefore, since no individual elements within it will be artificially capped, maximum choice will be given to family doctors and community nurses about how best to meet patient needs.

The role of a primary care group

A PCG will be responsible for:

- contributing to the health authority's health improvement programmes
- promoting the health of the local population
- commissioning health services for its population
- monitoring the services patients receive from NHS trusts
- developing primary care
- integrating primary and community health services
- working closely with social services.

The Government has indicated that the principle of GPs purchasing care is here to stay but that it is to be encouraged within an environment of co-operation rather than competition. In plans to be phased in from April 1999, GPs are to be given a choice of four commissioning models and these will replace the current range of fundholding and commissioning models. This is, of course, subject to legislation.

The choices available to family doctors are as follows:

- as a minimum advising and supporting their health authority in commissioning care for the local population

- acting as part of the health authority and taking devolved responsibility for managing budgets and sharing budgetary responsibility for health care in their area

- to form a free-standing primary care trust which acts as an independent group, accountable to the health authority, using devolved budgets to commission health care

- to form a free-standing primary care trust, accountable to the health authority, for commissioning care using a devolved budget with added responsibility for the provision of community services for the local population.

None of the above opportunities will affect the independent contractor status of GPs.

Links between health and social care

A number of important steps are proposed to promote more effective links and closer working between health and social care:

- plans to strengthen the duty of partnership between all parts of the NHS and social services

- new provision for local authority chief executives to participate in health authority meetings

- primary care groups to aim for greater collaboration with social services and involvement of local communities

- joint investment plans from 1999–2000 for continuing and community care.

The Government will consult during 1998 on further ways of achieving still closer local working relationships.

The patient and the receptionist

From the patient's view there are no major changes to services, since they are all still available, but should be more efficient as they are delivered according to the Patient's Charters. The Patient's Charter is a document setting out the standard of service to be provided in layman's language.

Receptionists arranging access to services will find that procedures depend on local arrangements, i.e. whether the particular service has gained trust status or whether it is still under the management of the health authority. Set procedures can only be specified by referring to the local offices of the ambulance service, social or community services. It is advisable for staff responsible for arranging transport to visit ambulance headquarters to see at first hand how requests for transport are processed.

As a result of the primary health care sector growing, the role of the receptionist, clerical and secretarial staff, both in the hospital and in general practice, is becoming increasingly complex as the changes are effected. No longer do staff merely 'go between' the doctor and patient, but must now liaise with hospital departments, community and social services. Every few months another department or service moves, changes its name, and its personnel change their function or role. It is important for all staff to understand the difficulties experienced in other sectors of health and social care provision as they cope with the fundamental changes going on around them.

Although doctors' surgery staff may have been recognized as part of the primary health care team for some time, their importance as key members in providing a communication link is growing with the size of the team and the increased variety of necessary points of contact. Similarly, surgery and hospital staff need to be aware of their new role as the government puts greater emphasis onto health promotion.

The primary health care team

The change of emphasis from institutionalized health care provision to management by smaller sections within the services generates a greater need for deliberate integration of the various services so that patients are presented with 'seamless' health and social care.

Staff increasingly become involved in dealing with queries, passing messages, and ensuring that the patients released from long-term institutionalized care, or fresh from surgical procedures, receive the service they need from the various members of the extended primary health care team.

From the 1960s, as health authorities built health centres, accommodation was provided for the community, social and other services, including chiropody, dental and dispensaries. This made it easier for doctors and receptionists to communicate with, for example, community staff, because they were likely to meet in the health centre. In the last few years there has been a general move to 'attach' community staff to specific surgeries where the premises are privately owned by the doctors. A message book is kept in reception so that messages can be picked up easily, and office space is made available.

The benefits of better communication have been supplemented by developing primary health care team meetings. These may have a strong clinical flavour, where doctors and health visitors, midwives and social workers discuss the needs of specific patients. Alternatively, meetings where strategies are developed for defining and maintaining management and administration of the team would also include reception and administration staff. It is essential to have a chair person to control the agenda so that the subject areas are of interest to everyone. Even if meetings are only held monthly, getting together a group of up to 40 people on a regular basis can be extremely difficult. It is important, therefore, to produce brief minutes so that those who are unable to attend can follow up issues with colleagues.

The primary health care team in its broadest sense includes doctors, practice manager, practice nurses, nurse practitioner, reception, secretarial and other administrative staff, health visitors, midwives, community nursing stafff, social workers, community psychiatric nurses and any other nursing specialists. Within this team, however, there are other teams, e.g. receptionists, practice nurses, practice secretaries and so on. Each team should work together for the common good, so it is important for each team member to appreciate the role, purpose and special skills of its members.

Since October 1997, *all* staff working in primary health care, including receptionists, secretaries and practice nurses, are eligible to contribute to the NHS Pension Scheme. This development has meant fewer staff changes in the practice team and has especially encouraged receptionists and secretaries to feel that their skills and experience are recognized and their employment offers a worthwhile career structure.

The general medical practitioner

The GP is at the centre of primary health care. The doctor's surgery represents the entrance to most of the services provided by the NHS and the GP's responsibility is to maintain the health of patients and their families by treatment, prevention and health education. GPs give personal and continuing care to their patients, and are in a position to build up a relationship of trust. They attend patients in their consulting room and in their homes. The GP aims to make initial diagnoses of problems presented, to provide treatment as appropriate, or where necessary to refer patients for further professional treatment.

Registrars (trainees)

If the general medical practice is a training practice, the registrar may be part of the medical team. Registrars are fully qualified doctors undergoing the requisite training and gaining expertise in general medical practice.

The practice manager

The practice manager is the person to whom both secretaries and receptionists in general practice are accountable. He/she has a central role in the day-to-day smooth running of the practice to ensure a quality service to the patients. The manager is the leader responsible for building, maintaining and co-ordinating the practice team so that the objectives are achieved and tasks completed satisfactorily. The manager also has the responsibility of developing and training individuals and helping them to realize their potential. They are the person secretaries and receptionists will go to to discuss any difficulties and problems experienced in the workplace.

Community nursing sisters

These used to be known as district nurses because they worked on a geographical basis looking after the nursing needs of patients in their own homes. They are now more often than not attached to a single practice and work with the patients belonging to that practice, or perhaps the patients of two smaller practices. Practice attachment gives them a chance to work more closely in a team with other staff but has the disadvantage of spreading their work over a very wide area. Occasionally these nurses work in the treatment room of the practice. They are employed by the health authority and are fully trained nurses who have experience in hospitals before coming to work in the community. They are involved in traditional nursing duties such as treating people who are ill at home with heart failure, acute chest conditions, terminal illness or, increasingly, after early discharge from hospital. These patients may require wound dressings, attention to bowels, prevention of bed sores and so on, and their relatives at home will gain great support from being taught how to help the patients themselves or just by knowing that someone will be coming in regularly.

Health visitors

The health visitor is a trained nurse with a post-registration qualification, employed by the health authority, and working mainly as a member of the primary health care team. The training of health visitors is rooted in the promotion of health and they learn to recognize the effects of psychological, social, economic and environmental factors on health and this enables them to fulfil their role in health education and the prevention of disease.

Although health visitors are concerned with all age groups, they have a special responsibility for the under-fives. New-born babies are visited in their own homes, and parents advised on matters of child health and development. Emphasis is given to the need for immunization and the value of attending a child health clinic. They are also concerned with other vulnerable groups such as the elderly, the physically and mentally handicapped, single parents, and families under stress. In addition they may be involved in the provision of health surveillance programmes and research, in which case an age–sex register or other form of database is particularly helpful.

Practice nurses

These form a rapidly growing group of health care workers and represent one way by which health services are changing to meet new challenges. They are usually employed by the practice and do most of their work within the treatment room. They are usually fully trained nurses who have had experience in hospital and other fields before taking up practice work. Practice nurses are employed in traditional work in the treament room such as applying dressings, giving injections, syringing ears and removing sutures. The range of their activity is changing to include helping to run health promotion clinics, assist with child health surveillance and minor surgery. They are thus often specially trained in the management of chronic illness such as asthma, diabetes and hypertension. Practice nurses are beginning to use some of the tools that were traditionally used only by the doctor such as ophthalmoscopes, stethoscopes, auriscopes and vaginal speculae. Further important extensions of their work involve counselling, listening and reassuring.

Nurse practitioners

Nurse practitioners are nurses with specialist training which allows them to practise independently. In some cases they take on responsibilities similar to those of junior medical staff and in general practice they may run clinics and assess priorities.

Midwives

Midwives have a central role in the care of pregnant women. They are fully trained nurses who have then completed a prolonged midwifery course. They are employed by the health authority and they form part of the team with hospital obstetricians, general practitioners and health visitors concerned with antenatal care, antenatal preparation, intrapartum care, delivery, and postpartum care of the mother and infant. They run antenatal clinics sometimes with doctors, and conduct normal deliveries in hospital and occasionally in the home. They are also very much involved in the postpartum care of mothers discharged home early after delivery.

Social workers

In about one in five consultations a doctor becomes involved in discussions and advice about personal relationships, work, social benefits, social support or other financial matters. These are important features of primary care, but just as the doctor will want to call on the special skills of nurses for some problems, so he will want to use a social worker's skills in the issues listed above.

If, for example, a young single mother is taken ill the problem extends beyond the immediate care of a sick woman and involves a healthy child also. If an elderly person living alone has a minor stroke which limits their independence by making it difficult to cook, clean or shop, another sort of problem arises that might best be solved by a home help, meals on wheels or laundry services. The social worker will help in assessing the need for this service, and in setting up these forms of care if they are needed. Again, if family tensions threaten dangers to the wife or children, supervision and counselling may be required and is most likely to be dealt with by a social worker.

There are some specialized social workers – these include psychiatric social workers who are important in the involuntary admission of the psychiatrically sick and in helping and supporting the long-term sick such as patients who are schizophrenics, or those with senile dementia who live in the community.

Community psychiatric nurses

Community psychiatric nurses belong to a profession which, although still in its infancy, is of increasing importance. Their role has developed with the trend towards rehabilitating and caring for the mentally infirm in the community. Although they may be used in psychiatric hospitals they are largely involved in providing support and treatment in collaboration with general practitioners. They tend to act as independant clinical practitioners themselves, backed by both consultants and general practitioners, with the object of restricting long-term hospital treatment to the severest cases only.

Pharmacists

We see in another section how doctors and pharmacists relate to each other in terms of their activities with prescriptions. Many patients go first to the pharmacist with their complaint and may never need to see the doctor. Others are advised by the pharmacist that a consultation is necessary. Communication between the two professions is very important.

Home helps

Home helps play a vital role in keeping the elderly in their homes for as long as possible. Their role is to perform those domestic tasks – such as shopping, washing, cleaning and collecting pensions – which the elderly can no longer undertake because of infirmity. They have no clinical responsibility but their visits provide a friendly and caring link with the outside world. It is usually the social services department of the local authority that organizes their work.

Other members

There is a large variety of other skilled workers who, from time to time, become part of the team. Experts like chiropodists, dieticians, physiotherapists, clinical psychologists, pharmacists and so on, may be involved.

The principal skill of clinical psychologists is in the realm of personal development and interpersonal relationship. They can help with behavioural problems of children and teenagers, getting people to cope with life's difficulties, marital problems and so on.

Home care teams

We have seen that some teams consist of people employed by the practice, whilst others consist of people employed by the health authorities. There is yet another arm of support – voluntary organizations. A particularly good example of this is the hospice providing care for the terminally ill. Doctors and nurses working in this field, supported mainly by charity, develop a particular expertize and have teams that can visit patients in their own homes by arrangement with the general practitioner.

Other members of the health care team

Physiotherapists diagnose and treat patients' difficulties with movement, especially joints, and assist with rehabilitation after injury. Until recently they worked mainly in hospitals, but an increasing number now work in the community. GPs have direct access to their services.

Social workers can help many patients with problems in non-medical areas of their lives, e.g. living conditions, debts or problems with relation-ships or child care. The intervention of social workers at an early stage can often help in tackling patients' problems, although these may be closely related to medical conditions for which they consult their doctor. In some areas, GPs employ their own social worker because of the support he/she can give to patients who visit their doctor because they do not know where elso to go.

Counsellors may be employed by GPs or attend their surgeries for designated sessions; early intervention by a counsellor who has time to listen to patients' non-medical problems can help to avert a critical situation.

Dieticians and other care staff advise on the best food and drink for particular medical conditions. Some health centres and GP practices have a dietician attending for designated sessions, working closely with members of the primary health care team.

Occupational therapists help patients to resume a normal life after mental or physical illness through activity-based treatments, and the pro-vision of aids to living. They will also assess what alterations are needed to enable elderly or disabled people to continue living at home.

Speech and language therapists help patients who have communication difficulties, especially after stroke or injury. They are trained to diagnose and treat all forms of speech disabilities, disorders of language and articu-lation in children.

Chiropodists play an important part in helping the elderly, who fre-quently have debilitating toe and foot problems, to maintain an active role in the community.

Audiometricians do much in helping those with hearing disabilities to live a normal and active life.

Other specialist nurses

Specialist nurses working in the community also include:

- school nurse
- stoma care nurse
- paediatric nurse
- geriatric nurse
- local authority clinic nurse.

The Terms of Service for family health services practitioners

General practitioners working in the NHS have a contract with the health authority or health board/health and social services board to provide general medical services for their NHS patients. Receptionists and secretaries should have an understanding of the main terms of service which may concern their daily work. The Terms of Service for doctors in general practice require a GP principal to:

- provide medical care to anyone whom he/she has accepted as a patient
- be available to his/her patients at all times or arrange a competent doctor to provide care in his/her absence
- be available at the surgery or visit patients at times agreed with the health authority. A full-time principal is expected to work at least 26 hours each week (this does not include on-call)
- offer in writing to patients aged 75 years and over an annual consultation and a domiciliary visit, to assess whether any treatment is required
- a consultation within 28 days of registration to all newly registered patients
- provide premises adequate for the delivery of medical care
- employ staff who are suitably qualified and competent to undertake the duties required of them
- ensure that practice staff receive continuing training
- provide a practice information leaflet for patients

- send an annual report to the health authority giving details of the staff, premises, use of hospital services and prescribing arrangements
- have in place and operate a practice-based complaints procedure
- have a written Practice Charter.

In 1995, the Department of Health agreed changes to the terms and conditions of the contract which made it easier for GPs not to see patients out-of-hours. GPs are now able to opt out of organizing and providing 24-hour care altogether as long as another GP has been identified who will provide that service to their patients. In the past GPs were paid a higher fee if they covered their own patients out-of-hours and if they visited them in their own home rather than asking them to come to the surgery. However, there is now a single fee for night visits and GPs get the same rate for seeing any patient whether or not they are on their list and whether they are seeing them at home or at the surgery.

Co-operatives

Many GPs are forming rotas to share on-call work. The GP co-operatives usually involve more than 10 GPs and generally vary in size from 15 GPs to more than 200, covering areas from small towns to a hundred miles or so.

Deputizing services

Some practices are making greater use of deputizing services which are run by private companies whereby GPs pay the service a fee and the deputizing service arranges for another GP to cover their patients out-of-hours.

Emergency centres

Many co-operatives and deputizing services have set up emergency centres where patients have to travel to, or are able to telephone, for advice. These centres may be based at a local practice, in a local hospital or in a purpose-built building. They cover a number of practices and are staffed by GPs and, occasionally, also by practice nurses.

Health promotion

Approximately 20 years ago, health education was a new field seeking to make information about health matters available to anyone who wanted it. Health education councils generated literature, visited surgeries, schools and hospitals, to circulate information. In the last five years there has been an increase in health promotion in doctors' surgeries which has supplemented health education. Every opportunity is taken to draw attention to health issues, advise individuals to bring them to a point of decision to make changes in their lifestyle and then give out literature to further educate on how and why to make changes. Health promotion draws attention to the need to change, and educates sufficiently to enable a patient to make an informed choice to change. Support during the change process and further education with literature must then follow. The terms 'education' and 'promotion' refer to different aspects, but to effect change in patient behaviour the two must work hand in hand.

General practitioners and health care providers have been required to extend their services into promotion of health, as well as looking after the sick. Surgeries have implemented health promotion clinics, such as well-man and well-woman, where patients are asked details of their lifestyle and given advice on how they might prevent ill-health by changes to diet, drinking habits, smoking, exercise and so on. Where needs such as help in giving up smoking are identified, specific clinics are then provided in some surgeries, so that patients benefit from peer group support.

However, all the primary health care team, including receptionists and secretaries, are now required to be far more aware of promoting health. Just as one would find it difficult to accept advice from an obviously overweight practice nurse advising that one must lose at least two stones in weight in the next six months, it is important that health care staff present a healthy image – which may include not being seen smoking – to back up the message that the practitioners and other health professionals give out daily.

Patient waiting areas should be used to the full to promote health, with good quality notices tidily pinned up on notice boards, and to educate by leaflets available for patients to read whilst waiting or to take home. It may be the practice nurse's responsibility to maintain notice boards and supplies of leaflets, but it is important that receptionists keep their eyes open and draw the nurse's attention to notice boards that are looking unkempt or leaflet supplies that are running low.

General practices have also found that 'open days' are an excellent opportunity to give out health promotion messages, when patients are invited into the surgery perhaps on a Saturday afternoon to have blood pressure and cholesterol checks, and so on.

The educational aspect is supported in most schools who ask health visitors and social workers to speak to children and answer questions about what they can do to help themselves. Schools may also invite specific organizations, such as ASH (anti-smoking) or local AIDS charities to educate students about their particular area of expertise.

Since there are 1001 sources of educational information the role of staff is to be aware of where materials can be obtained for a wide range of subjects, so that literature can be obtained without undue delay. Where literature is not free, details of costs might be kept on record along with the addresses and contact numbers.

The Government is making funding available for health promotion in surgeries by paying doctors who achieve targets for health promotion, but it is very difficult to audit the results. The range of effects on individual lives that might contribute to ill health makes it impossible to generalize about how effective any one particular message might have been. However, research to date shows that eating 'healthily', regular exercise and moderation in alcohol intake, along with refraining from smoking, all contribute to remaining healthier for longer. Where large scale health promotion in partnership with health education has been government sponsored, as in Finland, treatment for and deaths from heart disease have been reduced.

Therefore, it is part of the role of the receptionist to support initiatives to promote better health, not only by being aware of the advice given out by doctors and health professionals, but advising patients to attend health promotion clinics or events put on by the surgery, and by themselves presenting a healthy image to patients.

Local authority social services

Major local authorities have a social services committee, with an appointed director in charge of its social services department, who co-ordinates and administers the authority's social services.

Secretaries and receptionists inevitably will be asked by patients for information and advice about social services provision, and should be in a position of having the relevant information readily available to deal with such queries in a helpful, positive way.

Structure and social services provided

Figure 12.1 demonstrates the structure of a typical social services department. The organization of the department will vary from area to area, but there are usually at least five main sections of a social services department:

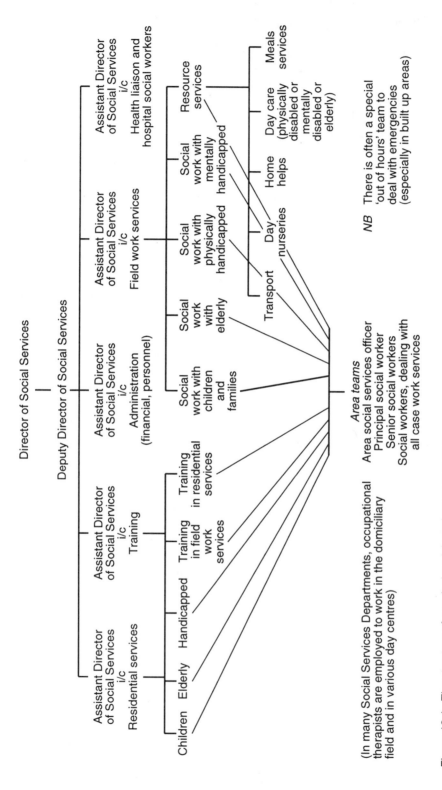

Figure 12.1 The structure of a typical social services department.

- residential services
- field work services
- provision of training facilities
- hospital social work
- administration.

The following is a summary of services provided by social services committees:

- *Care of the elderly* – This includes both field work services carried out within the community and residential care.

- *Care of the physically handicapped* – Blind, deaf, dumb, hearing difficulties, spastic, epileptic, paraplegics and other disabled persons.

- *Social work advice to the homeless* – Provision of permanent accommodation, care of homeless families, advice and help on prevention of homelessness, bed and breakfast accommodation.

Note: Those who are homeless are 'priority'. 'Priority' means anyone who has one or more children living with them; anyone who is made homeless, e.g. fire or flood; any household which includes one or more people who are elderly or mentally/physically handicapped, or suffer from physical disability; battered wifes; pregnant women. The homeless are also divided into those made *homeless by chance* and those made *homeless intentionally.*

- *Child care services* – Child care protection/supervision; acceptance of parental responsibility for children committed into care of the local authority; control of residential units; admission units; reception centres; residential nurseries; children's homes; community homes with education on the premises and classifying homes; adoption services; child abuse/prevention of child abuse services.

- *Social work and family case work dealing with mental disorder* – Provision of social workers; adult training centres; workshops; residential accommodation (hostels).

- *Day care for children under five years of age* – Provision of day nurseries, supervision of private nurseries and childminders.

- *Provision of home carers.*

- *Care of unsupported mothers* – Including residential care.

- *Hospital social workers* – Provision of social work services for hospital patients.

- *Work in the field of alcohol and drug abuse.*

Social work teams

A team of area social workers undertake all the case work for family and clients, so that problems can be considered as a whole, thus leading to family social services, helping all kinds of social problems in the family. Teams are made up of specialist social workers, for example, specialists in child care, mental illness or handicap, physical handicap and in the care of the elderly. It is the area social work team which usually co-ordinates the allocation of:

- home carers
- meals on wheels
- day nursery places
- vacancies in residential homes for the elderly
- residential accommodation for children.

Health and social services liaison

Social services work in close liaison with the local health authority to provide support and help in the community to patients recently discharged from hospital, or suffering from a disabling condition. The necessary adaptations, gadgets and aids for these people that are vital for their rehabilitation are supplied by the occupational therapy section of the social services department.

A community physician, who is a specialist in community medicine, is responsible for liaison between health and social services. Social workers now visit medical practices and health centres, where they meet general practitioners, health visitors, community nurses and school nurses working from these centres.

Community care

Social services departments will continue to work closely with health authorities to plan and provide 'care packages' to give the support people need to help in their daily lives, and may be available from local government and health authorities. It involves both social and health care and the Government will continue to encourage purchasers and providers to work with local authority partners to ensure that arrangements for community care work effectively. One of the major aims of community care is to enable people to maximize their independence by living in their own home for as long as possible, and when this is no longer practicable, to find them a homelike place to live.

Mental health services

Local authorities provide a wide range of services, including community care services, for people requiring mental health services. Local community care charters give information about the services and standards expected from local social services departments which help to ensure higher standards of social care for people with mental illness.

Local authorities should have a charter covering community services for people with mental health problems which are responsive to local needs. Patients and carers have a right to know what community care services are available and the standards of performance they can expect to receive. Community care charters should cover information about:

• assessments and care management

• performance standards for services

• how to complain

• how local authorities monitor performance.

Care Programme Approach

The Care Programme Approach is the way specialist mental health services are delivered to those who need them and patients can expect:

• an assessment of their health and social care needs

• a written plan to meet those needs

• to be involved in drawing up their care plan

• a regular review of their care plan

• to have a named mental health worker (care co-ordinator or key-worker) who is responsible for patients' care under the Care Programme Approach.

New rights for carers

From 1 April 1996, carers were given new rights under a new law called the Carers Recognition and Services Act (otherwise known as the Carers Act). The Act entitles carers to an assessment in their own right. Social services departments will have to listen to carers, record their views and take into account the result of the carer's assessment when they decide what services to bring to the person who is being cared for. The Carers Act says that carers are people who look after and support sick, elderly and disabled relatives and friends, providing a substantial amount of care on a regular basis.

Summary

The foregoing is intended to stress the importance to secretaries and receptionists of having sources of information at their finger-tips so that they are able to answer, with knowledge and understanding, the numerous and diverse questions put to them by patients and their relatives.

13

Audit and health economics for the medical receptionist and secretary

Introduction

Receptionists and secretaries working in the health care field will no doubt be aware of the emergence of new concepts and buzzwords or phrases for a wide variety of initiatives and processes, all aimed to benefit the patient. The most important of these issues is considered to give the reader an underpinning knowledge and understanding of concepts influencing the NHS today.

Audit

Receptionists and secretaries in their day-to-day activities can consider what they do and if they can do it better to provide a quality service to patients.

1 Identifying or defining criteria and standards in order to answer the question 'What are we doing/trying to achieve for our patients?'
2 Collecting data on current performance, i.e. the care and/or service given and its effects on patients. Are they satisfied?

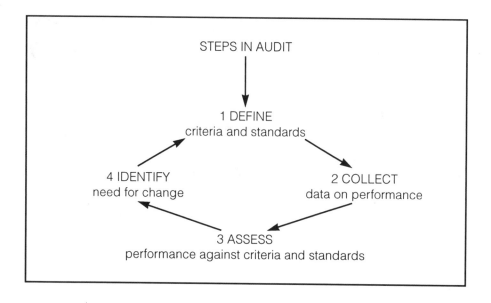

3   Assessing performance against criteria to determine whether standards have been met and objectives achieved.
4   Identifying the need for change or improvement in patient care.

The importance of audit

Decision making can only be truly effective when it is based on accurate record keeping and information about various activities, for example, receptionists may be asked to keep records of numbers of patients seen at the surgery or in the hospital clinic. This is important in decision making to improve the quality of care or service to patients:

*   to introduce a new clinic

*   to extend the length of the surgery or clinic

*   to check that the current consultation system is working satisfactorily in the best interests of both doctors and patients

*   to increase staffing levels.

Secretaries and receptionists may feel that the information or statistics kept to help decision making is never ending, but it must be remembered that the conclusions drawn may affect all members of the team, and foster a feeling of team spirit and involvement. This in turn will create a professional and caring team playing an important part in the delivery of a high standard of service and health care.

Health economics and cost-effective medicine

Although it is appreciated that readers of this book are unlikely to become involved in these processes, an insight will provide an understanding of some of the dominant political and economic issues facing the NHS and health care today. The UK like many other nations has experienced a rapid increase in health care expenditure, and with it health economics.

Health economics

Economics is concerned with the way in which people earn their living and how they spend their earnings, particularly on goods an services. Health economics is defined as how resources are allocated to health-related issues and the increasing cost of providing a quality health care system. As expenditure on health care has increased dramatically over the past 30 years, it is not surprising that health economics has emerged as a speciality in its own right and has shown a rapid expansion.

Economics can be divided into two main areas:

- macroeconomics
- microeconomics.

Macroeconomics is concerned with the functioning of the whole economy. Microeconomics is concerned with the functioning of individual parts of the economic system, e.g. the price of a particular product or service, or the behaviour of an individual organization/institution and so on. Health care is part of the microeconomic system concerned with the effects of expenditure in supplying the needs and demands made upon it. It focuses the choices made by individuals within the health system.

Evidence-based and cost-effective medicine

The philosophy of evidence-based medicine is one on which the medical profession may base the practice of medicine by using a model designed to help provide a treatment or service which is of benefit to, and in the best interests of, patients, yet at the same time considers the cost-effectiveness of such treatment. It is based on evidence resulting from medical research and outcomes of clinical audit. Consideration is given to the cost of providing such treatment, the availability of funds and the quality of patient care.

Private Finance Initiative

The Private Finance Initiative, first announced in the 1992 Budget, is intended to harness private sector management expertise and efficiency in delivering public services. In the NHS it has included the building and ser-vicing of new district general hospital facilities as well as a range of smaller projects.

The scheme enables the NHS to harness private sector expertise allow-ing NHS management to concentrate on delivering cost-effective clinical services ultimately providing better value for money.

Conclusion

While not directly involved in the concepts discussed in this chapter, receptionists and secretaries are an integral part of a health care team which is committed to providing patients with high quality and cost-effective care. It is important to remember that every member of the team is involved in collecting the data necessary to assess the quality of care and if change is indicated as an outcome of audit, then teamwork is essen-tial to achieving the wider context of quality in health care provision.

14
—

Training and development

Training and development should also be considered as ways of improving your personal effectiveness. Before we consider this in more detail, it is important to distinguish between:

- training
- education
- development.

Training is a systematic process for developing the skills, knowledge and attitudes, applied to a specific type of work. It is the process of bringing a person to an agreed standard of competence by practice or instruction.

Education is the process of acquiring background knowledge and skills. It does not have to be specific to a particular area of work.

Development is a course of action which enables individuals to realize their potential for growth and promotion in an organization.

Well-trained receptionists and secretaries are valued members of the work team, and are better able to understand, value and contribute to the smooth running of the medical practice or hospital department.

Excellent training courses are available and may be provided as in-house training taking place in the work environment, or by external training providers, for example, health authorities and colleges of further education (see Appendix 3). Training courses leading to a recognized qualification may necessitate attendance at a college on a day release basis, or may be provided as short training courses taking place in the evening.

Why train?

The reasons for training staff are varied, but generally they will fall into one of the following categories:

- induction needs of new staff

  - introduction to the practice, the practice team and practice objectives

  - information about the workplace and conditions of employment

  - initial job training

- to help staff improve their performance at work

  - where staff need further training to enable them to do their job at the required level of competence

- further job training

  - to give fuller job-related training in specific areas/tasks

- personal development

  - training provided where staff wish to develop their career, e.g. by attending a course to gain a professional qualification

- re-training

  - where the nature of the job changes and re-training is necessary to enable the individual to carry out the new work competently

- policy implementation

  - staff training may be necessary to ensure that national criteria are implemented

- response to organizational change

  - training is necessary where staff are required to respond to changes affecting their jobs, e.g. introduction of new technology, improving teamwork, teambuilding, etc.

Training strategies

There are five main training strategies appropriate to the needs of receptionists and secretaries:

- on-the-job: may be carried out by immediate supervisor in the workplace

- planned organizational experience: in-house training, e.g. special project to investigate a problem (appointments system not working well) and make recommendations for improvement

- in-house courses: suitable for short-term training needs to target a specific area and carried out by immediate supervisor or an external trainer

- off-the-job (external courses): regular attendance at a college or training centre offering specific courses/qualifications

- open/distance learning: training courses designed to give greater flexibility and suitable where regular attendance is impractical.

Self-development

Self-development is the development of yourself, by yourself through a deliberate process of learning from experience. This definition assumes that you need to organize it for yourself, rather than expect other people to be responsible for your development. If you don't take responsibility for your own development, who else will? The door to development is locked – you are the keyholder!

Your manager is responsible for providing you with development opportunities but it is always up to the individual to take the opportunities on offer and make something of them.

National vocational qualifications (NVQs)

More and more training and development programmes and learning materials are designed to provide the underpinning knowledge and understanding which facilitates the achievement of competence towards NVQs (SNVQs in Scotland).

NVQs (and SNVQs) are based on what people need to be able to do to carry out their jobs competently – they are work-based competences, which are assessed in the workplace. The qualifications are based on completion of units and elements and achievement of stated standards of performance criteria.

NVQs (and SNVQs) are assessed on the production of evidence of achievement, and secretaries and receptionists wishing to achieve NVQs (or SNVQs) should gather evidence in the form of a 'portfolio'. A portfolio is a collection of evidence demonstrating competence which can be based on previous as well as current learning.

Career structure

Secretaries and receptionists working in the field of health care are in a position, with their experience and further training, to progress to achieve the position of senior secretary or receptionist, and could well be considered sufficiently competent to progress further to a supervisory or management role within the organization.

An opportunity to discuss career development and any training needs could be identified at your annual performance appraisal, and a personal development plan arranged.

Summary

Training and development contribute to developing your personal effectiveness as a medical secretary or receptionist, and also to being a more effective, highly valued member of the work team.

There are several professional organizations and associations offering recognized qualifications. Your practice manager, training manager or your local college will be able to provide you with further information.

Further reading and reference books

Medical secretaries and receptionists should know the sources from which information can be obtained. The following list will be of value.

Medical reference

- *Medical Dictionary – Dorland's Pocket Medical Dictionary*
  Pocket Medical Dictionary, Churchill Livingstone.

- *The Medical Directory* – Consists of two volumes containing a directory of all qualified medical practitioners with addresses, qualifications and posts held. Information about hospitals is also included. There will usually be a recent copy at your place of employment.

- *First Aid Manual* – The authorized manual of St John's Ambulance Association, St Andrew's Ambulance Association and the British Red Cross Society.

- *British National Formulary* – This contains accurate information about all proprietary drugs.

- *MIMS* – A monthly publication listing all proprietary drugs and their uses.

General reference

English

- *The Concise Oxford Dictionary* or *Chambers Dictionary*

- Fowler's *Modern English Usage* – A helpful reference book for problems relating to English usage and grammar.

- Roget's *Thesaurus of English Words and Phrases* – This book lists words according to their meaning.

Information about correct forms of address will assist the secretary in ascertaining decorations, honours and qualifications, and placing them in the correct sequence. For example:

- Black's *Titles and Forms of Address*
- Debrett's *Peerage and Baronetage*
- *Who's Who*.

Travel information/guides

The secretary may find the following helpful, but up-to-date information should always be obtained from appropriate sources:

- Railway and Airways Guides
- Railway timetables
- Automobile Association (AA) and Royal Automobile Club (RAC) – These handbooks given useful information for motorists and details of hotels, etc.

Addresses and telephone numbers

Reference can be made to telephone directories and *Yellow Pages* for addresses and telephone numbers and listings of names under professions or trades.

The Post Office Directory can be used for detailed information of streets and occupiers of each house/shop etc.

General

- *Whitaker's Almanac*
- *Guide to your Local Social Services Provision*
- *Post Office Guide*
- *Voluntary Services Guide*
- *Pear's Cyclopaedia*.

Further reading

Debell B (1997) *Conciliation and Mediation in the NHS: a practical guide*. Radcliffe Medical Press, Oxford.
Dixon M, Murray T and Jenner D (eds) (1998) *The Locality Commissioning Handbook: from vision to reality*. Radcliffe Medical Press, Oxford.

Ellis N (ed) (1997) *General Practitioners Handbook*. Radcliffe Medical Press, Oxford.

Ellis N and Chisholm J (1997) *Making Sense of the Red Book* (3rd ed). Radcliffe Medical Press, Oxford.

Ham C (1997) *Management and Competition in the NHS* (2nd ed). Radcliffe Medical Press, Oxford.

Irvine D and Irvine S (eds) (1997) *Making Sense of Audit* (2nd ed). Radcliffe Medical Press, Oxford.

Irvine S and Haman H (1997) *Making Sense of Personnel Management* (2nd ed). Radcliffe Medical Press, Oxford.

Lindsay J and Ellis N (1998) *Staff Pensions in General Practice*. Radcliffe Medical Press, Oxford.

Robbins M and Weatherfield J (1994) *Terminology for Medical Administrators*. Radcliffe Medical Press, Oxford.

Practice Manager Library series:
Longridge L (1998) *Managing and Communicating: your questions answered.* Radcliffe Medical Press, Oxford.

Longridge L (1998) *Finance and Administration: your questions answered.* Radcliffe Medical Press, Oxford.

Longridge L (1998) *Premises and Information Technology: your questions answered*. Radcliffe Medical Press, Oxford.

APPENDIX 2

Hippocratic Oath

I swear by Apollo the physician, and Aesculapius and health and All-Heal and all the gods and goddesses, that, according to my ability and judgement, I shall keep this Oath and stipulation – to reckon him who taught me this Art equally dear to me as my parents, to share my substance with him and relieve his necessities if required, to look upon his offspring as my own brothers, and to teach them this Art, if they shall wish to learn it, without fee or stipulation, and that by precept, lecture and every other mode of instruction, I shall impart knowledge of the Art of my own sons, and those of my teachers, and to disciplines bound by stipulations and oath, according to the law of medicine but to none others. I will follow that system which, according to my judgement, I consider for the benefit of my patients and abstain from whatever is harmful for them. I shall give no deadly medicine to anyone if asked, nor suggest any such consent and in like manner I shall not advise a woman to procure abortion. With purity and holiness I shall pass my life and prac-tise my Art. Into whatever houses I enter, I shall go into them for the benefit of the sick. Whatever I see or hear, in the life of men, which ought not to be spoken abroad, I shall not divulge, as reckoning that all such should be kept secret.

Training programmes

The following are a selection of the principal nationally validated training programmes appropriate to receptionists and secretaries working in the field of health care.

Radcliffe Medical Press Ltd
18 Marcham Road
Abingdon
Oxon OX14 1AA
Tel: 01235 528820

Practice Receptionist Programmes 1, 2 and 3
Hospital Receptionist Programmes 1 and 2
Dental Receptionist Programmes 1 and 2

These training programmes can be used to provide significant evidence and underpinning knowledge for the NVQ (Administration) Level 2. PRP and HRP certificates are awarded on satisfactory completion of courses which are also available as distance/open learning training programmes.

Healthcare Supervisory Development

A distance learning programme designed to bridge the gap between NVQ Level 2, Administration and Level 4, Management. A National Certificate in Healthcare Supervision is awarded on satisfactory completion of the programme.

Association of Medical Secretaries, Practice Managers, Adminstrators and Receptionists (AMSPAR)

AMSPAR
Tavistock House North
Tavistock Square
London WC1H 9LN
Tel: 0171 387 6005

Diploma in Medical Reception
Diploma in Medical Secretarial Duties
Diploma in Practice Management

RSA Examinations Board – Medical Audio-Typing
Medical Shorthand
Medical Word Processing

Examinations and certificates at different levels

RSA Examinations Board
Westwood House
Westwood Way
Coventry
Warks CV4 8HS
Tel: 01203 470033

National Traineeship
National Traineeship is a new initiative providing an option for young people who want to continue in full-time work and train towards vocational qualifications (NVQ Level 2 – Care) in health and social care. National Traineeships provide a structured programme of work-based training and are supported by professional carers and trainers.

Medical terminology

Some components of words referring to body structures

A knowledge of these words will help you to deduce the meanings of many of the medical terms you hear and see in the course of your work.

Word	Pertaining to
aden	gland
angi	vessels (esp. blood vessels)
arthr	joint(s)
aur	ear(s)
cardi	heart
caud	tail
cephal	head
cheil	lip(s)
chole	biliary system
cholecyst	gall-bladder
chondr	cartilage
col	colon
cyst	bladder
derm	skin
enter	intestine
fibr	fibrous tissue
gastr	stomach
gloss	tongue
haem or aem	blood
hepat	liver
hyster	uterus
labi	lips
lymph	lymphatic system
mamm, mast	breast(s)
myel	bone marrow or spinal cord
myo	muscle(s)
nephr	kidney(s)
ocul, ophthal	eye
onych	nails
orch, orchid	testes
or	mouth

os, oste	bone(s)
ot	ear(s)
pneumon	lung(s)
proct	rectum
pyel	kidney pelvis
ren	kidneys
rhin	nose
salping	uterine tubes
sial	salivary glands
spondyl	vertebra(ae)

Suffixes

Suffix	Meaning	Term	Definition
-algia	pain	arthralgia	joint pain
-ac	pertaining to	cardiac	pertaining to the heart
-al			
-ar		vascular	relating to blood vessels
-ary		coronary	pertaining to the heart
-ic	referring to	pelvic	relating to the pelvis
-ory		sensory	pertaining to feeling
-ous	denoting	cutaneous	pertaining to the skin
-aemia	blood	hyperglycaemia	high blood sugar
-cele	swelling, hernia	cystocele	hernia of the bladder
		myelocele	protrusion of spinal cord through vertebrae
-centesis	puncture	paracentesis	puncture of a cavity
		thoracocentesis	aspiration of pleural cavity
-cyte	cell	leucocyte	white blood cell
-desis	binding fixation	arthodesis	surgical fixation of a joint
-dynia	pain	pleurodynia	pain in the intercostal muscles
-ectasis	dilation	atelectasis	abnormal dilation of bronchus or bronchi
-ectomy	removal, excision	tonsillectomy	removal of tonsils
-genic	origin	bronchogenic	originating in bronchi
-genesis	forming, producing	pathogenesis	producing disease
-gram	tracing, recording	venogram	recording (X-ray) of veins
-graphy	process of recording	arteriography	X-ray of arteries
-iasis	condition of, presence, formation of	lithiasis	formation of stones
		cholelithiasis	formation of stones in gall-bladder
-itis	inflammation	carditis	inflammation of heart

		rhinitis	inflammation of mucous membrane of nose
-logy	study of	cytology	study of cells
-malacia	softening	osteomalacia	softening of bone
-megaly	enlargement	cardiomegaly	enlargement of heart
-oid	like, resembling	osteoid	like bone
-oma	tumour	osteoma	tumour of bone
-osis	disease, abnormal condition	spondylosis	disease of spine
-pathy	disease	myelopathy	disease of spinal cord
-penia	lack of	leucopenia	deficiency of white blood cells
-phasis	ability to speak	dysphasia	difficulty in speaking
-phagia	ability to swallow	dysphagia	difficulty in swallowing
-phobia	fear of	agoraphobia	fear of open spaces
-pnoea	breath	dyspnoea	difficulty in breathing
-rrhage	a bursting out	haemorrhage	an escape of blood from the vessels
-stasis	arrest, or cessation, a halting	haemostasis	the arrest of a flow of blood
-trophy	nourishment	atrophy	to waste away
-uria	pertaining to urine	haematuria	presence of blood in urine

Prefix

Prefix	Meaning	Term	Definition
a-	absence, lack of	amnesia	loss of memory
ab-	from, away from	abduct	move away from mid-line of body
ad-	to, towards	adduct	move towards the mid-line of body
an-	absence, lack of	anaesthesia	loss of sensation
ante-	before	antepartum	before delivery
anti-	against	antiseptic	agent used against bacteria
brady-	slow	bradycardia	slow heart beat
contra-	opposite	contralateral	opposite side
circum-	around	cirumoral	around the mouth
com-	with	compound	to mix or fuse
con-	joined	congenital	present at birth
di-	disengage	diarthrosis	to separate from a joint
dia-	through, by means of		
ec-	out from	ectopic	not in normal place
endo	within	endometrium	lining of the uterus
exo-	outside	exogenous	produced outside

hypo-	beneath	hypotension	below normal blood pressure
infra-	under	infrapatellar	under the kneecap
inter-	between	intercostal	between the ribs
intra-	within	intracellular	within a cell
mega-	large, abnormally enlarged	megacolon	abnormally large (dilated) colon
micro-	abnormally small	microscopic	visible only with aid of microscope
onc-	pertaining to tumours	oncology	scientific study of tumours
para-	near, beside	paravertebral	beside the vertebra
peri-	around	pericardium	around the heart
pre-	forwards	prenatal	before birth
pro-	in front of	prognosis	forecast (of course of disease)
retro-	backwards	retroflexion	bending backward
sym-	beside	symphysis	growing together
syn-	along	synapse	joining of two neurons
tachy-	rapid	tachycardia	rapid heart beat
trans-	across	transurethral	through the urethra

Some of the most commonly used abbreviations

AID	artificial insemination donor
AIDS	acquired immune deficiency syndrome
APH	antepartum haemorrhage
ASD	atrial septal defect
ASD	autistic spectrum disorders
bd	twice per day
BI	bony injury
BP	blood pressure, British Pharmacopeia
CDH	congenital dislocation of the hip
CSF	cerebrospinal fluid
CNS	central nervous system
CT	computerized tomography
CAT	computerized axial tomography
CSU	catheter specimen of urine
CVP	central venous pressure
CVS	cardiovascular system
D&C	dilatation and curettage (uterine)
DLE	disseminated lupus erythematosus
DNA	did not attend (or deoxyribonucleic acid)
DS	disseminated sclerosis
DU	duodenal ulcer
D&V	diarrhoea and vomiting
DVT	deep vein thrombosis

DXRT	deep X-ray therapy
ECG	electrocardiography
EDD	expected date of delivery
ENT	ear, nose and throat
ESR	erythrocyte sedimentation rate
EUA	examination under anaesthetic
FB	foreign body
FHH	fetal heart heard
FDIU	fetal death in utero
GU	gastric ulcer
Hb	haemoglobin
HRT	hormone replacement therapy
IM	intramuscular
Ig	immunoglobulin
ISQ	in status quo (unchanged)
IUCD	intrauterine contraceptive device
IUD	intrauterine death or intrauterine (contraceptive) device
IV	intravenous
LB	loose body
MI	myocardial infarct
MRI	magnetic resonance imaging
MS	multiple sclerosis, mitral stenosis
MSU	midstream specimen of urine
NAD	no abnormality detected
NAI	non-accidental injury
NG	new growth
NYD	not yet diagnosed
OA	osteoarthritis
OT	occupational therapy
PET	positron emission tomography
PID	prolapsed intervertebral disc
PM	post mortem
POP	plaster of Paris
PPH	postpartum haemorrhage
PR	per (through) the rectum
PUO	pyrexia of unknown origin
PV	per (through) the vagina
RA	rheumatoid arthritis
RBC	red blood cell
RH	rhesus factor
SMR	submucous resection of nasal septum
SOB	shortness of breath
SOL	space-occupying lesion
SOS	if necessary
SPECT	single photon emission computer tomography
TB	tuberculosis or tubercle bacilli
tds	three times a day
THR	total hip replacement
TPR	temperature, pulse and respiration
Ts & As	tonsils and adenoids
TUR	transurethral resection (of prostate)

UTI	urinary tract infection
VD	venereal disease
VVs	varicose veins
WBC	white blood cells
WR	Wassermann reaction
XR	X-ray

Medical symbols

♀	male
♂	female
#	fracture
Δ	diagnosis
R_X	recipe (for prescription–"take thou")
+ve	positive
–ve	negative
c̄	with
s̄	without
1/7	one day
3/7	three days
1/52	one week
1/12	one month

Abbreviations used in prescribing

Abbreviation	Latin equivalent	English meaning
aa	ana	of each the amount
ac	ante cibum	before food
bd (or bid)	bis die (bis in die)	twice daily
c̄	cum	with
hn	hac nocte	tonight
mane	mane	in the morning
mdu	more dicta utendus	as previously directed
m et n	mane et nocte	morning and night
nocte	nocte	at night
om	omni mane	every morning
on	omni nocte	every night
pc	post cibum	after food
prn	pre re nata	whenever necessary
qds	quater die sumendum	four times a day
qid	quater in die	four times a day
sos	si opus sit	if necessary
stat	statim	immediately
td (or tid)	ter die (ter in die)	three times a day
tds	ter die sumendum	three times a day

Investigations

Digestive system

Test	Reason for test
Oral cytology	Detection of early cancer in the elderly
Oesophagoscopy (visual inspection of oesophagus)	Investigation of tumours, strictures Removal of foreign bodies
Gastroscopy (visual inspection of stomach)	Investigation of abnormalities, e.g. gastric ulcer, carcinoma
Liver function tests (LFTs)	Liver disease. Obstructive jaundice. Haemolytic jaundice
Endoscopic retrograde cholangio pancreatography (ERCP)	Detection of pancreatic cancer
Glucose tolerance tests (GTTs)	To test the patient's ability to stabilize his/her blood level
Laparoscopy (visual inspection of abdominal cavity)	Investigation of lower abdominal pain
Proctoscopy (visual inspection of anal canal and lower rectum)	Detection of haemorrhoids, or growths
Colonoscopy (visual inspection of colon)	Investigation of malignant changes or for biopsy
Sigmoidoscopy (visual inspection of sigmoid colon)	Detection of growths, ulcerative colitis
Examination of faeces	Diagnosis of gastric/duodenal ulcers/ carcinoma

Investigations and tests relating to haematology and blood transfusion

Test	Reason for test
Haemoglobin (Hb) estimation	Detection of abnormalities, e.g. poly-cythaemia, anaemia
Red cell count (RBC)	
Haematocrit or packed cell volume (PCV)	Routine blood investigations for presence of abnormalities
Mean corpuscular haemoglobin (MCH)	
Mean corpuscular haemoglobin concentration (MCHC)	
Erythrocyte sedimentation rate (ESR)	A test to screen for systematic disease (or progress of disease) e.g. inflammatory and autoimmune disease, malignancy, serious infection

White cell count (WBC)	Detection of disease and infection, e.g. pneumonia, leukaemia, appendicitis
Platelet count	Detection of disease, trauma, infection, inflammation, malignancy
Clotting time	To test extrinsic clotting system in diagnosis of haemophilia, obstructive jaundice, etc.
Prothrombin ratio	Investigation of haemorrhagic disorders, liver disease
Paul Bunnell	To diagnose infective mononucleosis (glandular fever)
Monospot	To diagnose infective mononucleosis (glandular fever)
Rose-Waaler (RA)	To diagnose rheumatoid arthritis
Latex fixation test	To diagnose rheumatoid arthritis
Antinuclear factor/antibody (ANF/ANA)	To diagnose systemic lupus erythematosus

Bacterial tests on blood

Widal reaction (WR)	Diagnosis of typhoid/paratyphoid and brucellosis
VDRL	Diagnosis of venereal disease
TPHA	Diagnosis of venereal disease
WR	Diagnosis of venereal disease
GCFT	Diagnosis of venereal disease
Guthrie's test	Estimation of blood level of phenylketonuria (PKU) in babies

---

Musculo–skeletal system

Disorders of bones and joints give rise to pain, deformity, swelling of bone and tissues, limitation of movement and secondary muscle wasting.

X-ray investigation is of value in diagnosis and assessment of response to treatment. Bone scanning is being increasingly used for detection of malignant conditions in bone.

Test	Reason for test
Arthroscopy (visual inspection of knee joint)	Diagnosis of disease/injury to interior of joint
Electromyography	Detection of muscular disorders, e.g. muscular dystrophy, myasthenia gravis and myotonia
Myelography	Detection of spinal lesions, e.g. tumours and prolapsed intervertebral disc
Radiculography	Similar procedure to myelography used to investigate the lumbosacral nerve roots

*(See also Miscellaneous investigations, page 263.)

Cardiovascular system

Test	Reason for test
Blood pressure (BP)	To detect disease Hypertension – abnormally high blood pressure Hypotension – abnormally low blood pressure
Angio-cardiography (injection of dye through catheter enabling X-ray of heart structure)	Detection of abnormalities of the heart and blood vessels
Electrocardiography (ECG) (recording of electrical activity of the heart)	To investigate heart disorders, e.g. coronary thrombosis, heart block
Echocardiography	Diagnosis of valvular disease and peri-cardial effusion

Respiratory system

Test	Reason for test
Rhinoscopy (examination of interior of nose)	Removal of tissue for histology, or swab taken for bacteriology
Laryngoscopy	Examination of vocal cords, larynx and epiglottis, for growths and infections
Bronchoscopy (visual inspection of bronchi)	Diagnosis of growths. Tissue removal for biopsy
Sputum examination	Examination of sputum for blood, parasites, etc.
Pleural fluid	Detection of malignancy, chest injury, emphysema, heart failure

Lung function tests

Test	Reason for test
Vital capacity of lungs (maximum amount of air which can be expired)	Measurement of amount of air expired by a patient. Diminished in lung disease
Wright's peak flow meter	Detection of lung disease

Nervous system

Test	Reason for test
Lumbar puncture	Examination of cerebrospinal fluid (CSF) and diagnosis of certain diseases of nervous system

Romberg's sign	Test for co-ordination. Used in diagnosis of multiple sclerosis, cerebral tumour, etc.
Kernig's sign	Diagnosis of meningitis, cerebral haemorrhage or meningism
Electroencephalogram (EEG)	Investigation of epileptic conditions and location of cerebral lesions
Electromyogram (EMG) (recording of electrical activity in a muscle)	Investigation of disease
Knee jerk	Detection of disease of nervous system

Pupil reflexes

Reaction to light	Detection of diseases of central nervous system

Eye tests

Optic discs	Detection of disease of central nervous system
Snellen's test	Measurement of extent of field of vision
Refraction tests	To correct defective vision by prescription of correct lens

Hearing tests

Audiometric tests	Determination of degree and type of hearing
Weber's test (tuning fork)	To distinguish between middle-ear and nerve deafness
Rinne's test	Detection of middle-ear deafness
Auriscopy (visual examination of middle ear)	Detection of infection and disease

---

Urinary system

Test	Reason for test
Routine laboratory examination	Detection of urinary infections, pyelonephritis. Haematuria (blood in urine)
Mid-stream specimen (MSU)	Nephritis, presence of parasites – tropical disease

Test for protein	Presence of protein in urine (albuminuria)
Test for sugar	Presence of sugar in urine (glycosuria)
Test for ketones	Presence of ketones in urine (ketonuria)
Test for blood	Presence of blood in urine (haematuria)

Renal efficiency tests

Blood urea	Impairment of renal function
Urea clearance test	To indicate extent of kidney damage
Cystoscopy (visual inspection of bladder)	Detection of disease of bladder. For biopsy of tissue/tumour
Intravenous pyelogram (IVP)	To test renal function. To demonstrate hydronephrosis, renal calculi, hydronephroma, etc.
Renal biopsy	Specimen sent for histology

Pregnancy tests

Oestriol examination	Assessment of both placental and fetal function
Toxaemia of pregnancy	Urine tested for protein – to confirm condition
Amniocentesis	Estimation of fetal maturity. Detection of fetal defects, etc.
Cervical smear	Early diagnosis of cancer. Detection of infection and other conditions
Vaginal swab	To detect cause of vaginal discharge

Endocrine glands

Test	Reason for test
Thyroid function tests (TFTs)	Assessment of functioning of thyroid glands
Protein bound iodine (PBI)	Measurement of thyroid function

X-ray investigations

Test	Reason for test
Barium swallow	Detection of lesions of oesophagus. Demonstration of hiatus hernia
Barium meal	Detection of lesions of stomach and duodenum
Barium meal with follow-through	Detection of lesions of small and large intestines
Barium enema	Detection of disease and obstruction of the bowel
Double contrast radiography	Detection of small changes in gastric mucosa, e.g. early carcinoma
Cholecystography	To demonstrate presence of gall stones
Intravenous cholangiogram	To demonstrate bile duct obstruction from growth or stones
Arthrogram	To outline joint cavity
Bone scan	Detection of secondary tumours
Angiography	Demonstration of obstruction, aneurysm or abnormal course (of blood vessel)
Aortogram	Angiogram of aorta
Arteriogram	Angiogram of arteries
Venogram	Angiogram of veins
Bronchography	Diagnosis of bronchiectasis and other bronchial abnormalities
Lung scan	Demonstration of tumours
Mammography	Detection of early malignancy of breast
Myelogram	Examination of spinal cord for obstruction and other defects
Encephalogram	Detection of cerebral tumours
Ventriculogram	To confirm cerebral tumour

Skin tests

Mantoux test	Skin test for sensitivity to TB by dilute intradermal injection of tuberculin
Heaf test	Similar to Mantoux, but using multiple-puncture technique
Kveim test	Intradermal injection to diagnose sarcoidosis

Miscellaneous investigations

Radiography

X-rays are one of the most frequently requested investigations used by physicians. They are painless unless used in conjunction with a contrast media, which may cause discomfort; they are quick and easy to perform, but may be frightening for the patient.

X-rays are a form of electromagnetic energy of a short wavelength which have the ability to penetrate tissues.

Plain X-rays are commonly carried out on the chest, the abdomen, skull and limbs in order to study bones for bone disease, fractures, etc. Contrast media may be used to visualize soft tissues and organs.

Ultrasonography (ultrasound)

Ultrasound is a non-invasive diagnostic procedure used to view body structures. It is convenient, safe and a comparatively inexpensive investigation. It does not use ionizing radiation and is thus safer than radiography. Ultrasound examinations are carried out on the following structures:

- the brain – electroencephalography

- the arteries and veins

- the heart – echocardiography

- the kidney, liver and pelvis.

In obstetrics its main use is to demonstrate fetal size and growth, and the position of the placenta.

Computerized tomography

Computerized tomography (CT) scanning is an X-ray technique which uses a computer to reconstruct an image of a layer of tissue in the body. The CT scanner can image the three main cavities of the body (head, thorax and abdomen). It is mainly used for detecting lesions such as tumours and cysts in the body.

A second generation CT system has evolved which produces three-dimensional images of the body. These latest 3D images allow doctors to examine, for example, a person's brain as if it were in their hands.

Nuclear magnetic resonance imaging (NMRI)

This form of investigation is now widely used in medicine, and is often referred to as MRI. It uses radio-frequency radiation in the presence of a magnetic field to produce anatomical sections of the human body.

It is a non-invasive technique, it does not use ionizing radiation, and it penetrates the structures of the body. In contrast with CT scanning, MRI can provide images in any anatomical plane.

Radioisotope scanning

A radioactive isotope is an unstable isotope which decays or disintegrates, emitting radiation or energy. The energy source is inside the patient and is given either orally or intravenously.

Radioisotopic scans are performed to detect malfunction or abnormalities of bones, lungs, brain, heart, kidneys, gall-bladder, spleen and endocrine glands.

Thermography

This is a technique which measures and records heat energy from the skin surface. It is non-invasive and causes no discomfort. Films are taken in much the same way as a photograph is taken, and plates with these films are placed on the skin and changes of skin temperature are reflected on a colour map.

Thermography is mainly used to detect lesions of the breast, to evaluate drug therapy, to diagnose spinal root compression, and may be used to assess the progress of wound healing.

Tomography

This is a technique in which a single layer of tissue is examined. This is achieved by blurring the image of the tissues above and below the layer of tissue to be studied when the X-ray is taken.

Fluoroscopy

Fluoroscopy enables the function of organs to be directly visualized in motion on a flourescent screen, e.g. the heart beat, movement of the diaphragm and motility of the gastrointestinal tract can be observed and recorded.

Immunization schedules

Recommended immunizations for children

The schedule below is currently recommended by the Department of Health.

AGE	DISEASE	METHOD
At birth (high risk infants only)	tuberculosis hepatitis B	injection (BCG) injection
4 weeks (high risk infants only)	hepatitis B	injection
2 months	diphtheria, tetanus pertussis *Haemophilus influenzae* type B (Hib) polio	one injection (DTP) injection by mouth (OPV)
3 months	diphtheria, tetanus pertussis *Haemophilus influenzae* type B (Hib) polio	one injection injection by mouth (OPV)
4 months	diphtheria, tetanus pertussis *Haemophilus influenzae* type B (Hib) polio	one injection (DTP) injection by mouth (OPV)
12–15 months (usually 14)	measles, mumps, rubella*	one injection (MMR)
4–5 years	diphtheria, tetanus polio	booster injection booster by mouth (OPV)
10–14 years (girls only)	rubella	one injection
13 years	tuberculosis	one injection (BCG)
15–19 years	polio	booster by mouth (OPV)
16–18 years (school leavers)	tetanus	one injection

*The Department of Health advises that children should not be given separate measles, mumps and rubella vaccines in place of MMR, since there is no evidence for benefit and a clear risk of harm from following such a practice.

Recommended immunizations for adults

DISEASE	FREQUENCY	METHOD
Tetanus toxoid	booster every 10 years	one injection, or 3 at monthly intervals for those previously unvaccinated
Polio	booster every 10 years until age 40	by mouth (OPV)
For at-risk groups		
Influenza	annually (especially for the elderly)	injection
Hepatitis B	booster every 3–5 years	injections (in first instance, 3 over 6 months, followed by blood test)

Vaccinations for foreign travel

Travellers to hot climates and developing countries should be given immunizations and anti-malarial advice according to up-to-date recommendations which can be found in the *Pulse* and *MIMS* charts published monthly, and the patient's previous immunization status.

Incubation periods of some infectious diseases

The incubation period is the interval between the time of primary infection or contact with an infected person, and the appearance of the disease. The following information is a guide only as in some instances some of the diseases have been found to have an incubation period outside that of the stated range.

DISEASE OR CAUSATIVE ORGANISM	INCUBATION PERIOD
Amoebic dysentery	1–4 weeks
Bacillus cereus enteritis	1–5 hours
Botulism	2 hours – 8 days (usually 12–36 hours)
Brucellosis	1–8 weeks (usually 2–3 weeks)
Campylobacter enteritis	1–11 days (usually 2–5 days)
Chickenpox	10–21 days (usually 14–15 days)
Cholera	2–48 hours
Dysentery	1–7 days (usually 1–3 days)
German measles (rubella)	14–21 days
Infective jaundice (hepatitis A)	14–42 days
Hepatitis B	42 days – 6 months
Lassa fever	3–17 days
Legionnaire's disease	2–10 days
Leptospirosis	4–19 days (usually 7–12 days)
Malaria	8–25 days
Measles	7–21 days (usually 10–14 days)
Mumps	12–28 days (usually 16–18 days)
Polio	10–15 days
Rabies	2 weeks–5 years (usually 20–90 days)
Salmonella enteritis	6–72 hours
Scarlet fever	2–5 days
Typhoid fever	7–21 days
Whooping cough	5–21 days
Yellow fever	3–6 days

Abbreviations of qualifying degrees and further qualifications

BAO	Bachelor of the Art of Obstetrics
BC, BCh, BChir	Bachelor of Surgery
BM	Bachelor of Medicine
BS, ChB, CChir	Bachelor of Surgery
BSc	Bachelor of Science
CCDC	Consultant in Communicable Disease Control
CM ChM	Master of Surgery
CPH	Certificate in Public Health
DA	Diploma in Anaesthetics
DCH	Diploma in Child Health
DCh	Doctor of Surgery
DCP	Diploma in Clinical Pathology
DDS	Doctor of Dental Surgery
DHyg	Doctor of Hygiene
DIH	Diploma in Industrial Health
DLO	Diploma in Laryngology and Otology
Dip Med Rehab	Diploma in Medical Rehabilitation
DM	Doctor of Medicine
DMR	Diploma in Medical Radiology
DO	Diploma in Ophthalmology
DObstRCOG	Diploma in Obstetrics of the Royal College of Obstetricians and Gynaecologists
DOMS	Diploma in Ophthalmological Medicine and Surgery
DPH	Diploma in Public Health
DPM	Diploma in Psychological Medicine
DR	Diploma in Radiology
DSc	Doctor of Science
DTH	Diploma in Tropical Hygiene
DTM	Diploma in Tropical Medicine
FDS	Fellow of Dental Surgery
FFA	Fellow of the Faculty of Anaesthetists
FFHom	Fellow of Faculty of Homeopathy
FFR	Fellow of the Faculty of Radiologists
FRCGP	Fellow of the Royal College of General Practitioners

FRCOG	Fellow of the Royal College of Obstetricians and Gynaecologists
FRCP	Fellow of the Royal College of Physicians of London
FRCPE	Fellow of the Royal College of Physicians of Edinburgh (may also be written as FRCPEd, FRCPEdin)
FRCPS	Fellow of the Royal College of Physicians and Surgeons
FRCPath	Fellow of the Royal College of Pathologists
FRCPsych	Fellow of the Royal College of Psychiatrists
FRCS	Fellow of the Royal College of Surgeons of England
FRCSE	Fellow of the Royal College of Surgeons of Edinburgh
FRIPHH	Fellow of the Royal Institute of Public Health and Hygiene
FRS	Fellow of the Royal Society
HVCert	Health Visitors Certificate
LAH	Licentiate of Apothecaries Hall, Dublin
LDS	Licentiate in Dental Surgery
LM	Licentiate in Midwifery
LRCP	Licentiate of Royal College of Physicians
LSA	Licentiate of Society of Apothecaries
MAO	Master of the Art of Obstetrics
MB	Bachelor of Medicine
MS, MCh, MChir	Master of Surgery
MChD	Master of Dental Surgery
MChOrth	Master of Orthopaedic Surgery
MCPath	Member of College of Pathology
MCPS	Member of College of Physicians and Surgeons
MD	Doctor of Medicine
MDS	Master of Dental Surgery
MFCP	Member of Faculty of Community Physicians
MFHom	Member of Faculty of Homeopathy
MHyg	Master of Hygiene
MMSA	Master of Midwifery of Society of Apothecaries
MPH	Master of Public Health
MRCGP	Member of Royal College of General Practitioners
MRCOG	Member of Royal College of Obstetricians and Gynaecologists
MRCP	Member of Royal College of Physicians of London
MRCPath	Member of Royal College of Pathologists
MRCPsych	Member of Royal College of Psychiatrists
MRCS	Member of Royal College of Surgeons of England
MS	Master of Surgery
RGN	Registered General Nurse
SEN	State Enrolled Nurse
SRN	State Registered Nurse
SRP	State Registered Physiotherapist

Other medical abbreviations (including job titles, organizations and non-clinical terms)

AHCPA	Association of Health Centres and Practice Administrators
AMSPAR	Association of Medical Secretaries, Practice Managers, Administrators and Receptionists
BAMM	Association of Medical Managers
BMA	British Medical Association
BMJ	British Medical Journal
BNF	British National Formulary
BP	British Pharmacopoeia
BPC	British Pharmaceutical Codex
BRCS	British Red Cross Society
CEM	cost-effectiveness based medical decision making
CHC	Community Health Council
CMB	Central Midwives Board
CME	continuing medical education
CNO	Chief Nursing Officer
CPA	Care Programme Approach
CRES	cash-releasing efficiency savings
DDA	Dangerous Drugs Act
DHA	District Health Authority
DN	District Nurse
DoH	Department of Health
DSS	Department of Social Security
EBM	evidence-based medicine
ECR	extra-contractual referral
EDI	electronic data interchange
EPR	electronic paper record
FHSA	Family Health Services Authority
FPA	Family Planning Association
GDP	General Dental Practitioner
GMC	General Medical Council
GMSC	General Medical Services Committee
GMP	General Medical Practitioner
HAZ	Health Action Zone
HCHS	hospital and community health services
HIP	Health Improvement Programme
HV	Health Visitor
IHSM	Institute of Health Services Management
IMA	Independent Medical Adviser
LMG	Local Medical Committee
MAAG	Medical Audit Advisory Group
MDU	Medical Defence Union
MIMS	Monthly Index of Medical Specialities
MPS	Medical Protection Society
MSW	Medical Social Worker
NAHAT	National Association of Health Authorities and Trusts

NBTS	National Blood Transfusion Service
NHS	National Health Service
OT	Occupational Therapist
PACT	Prescribing Analysis and Costs
PCG	Primary Care Group
PCLM	Primary Care Liaison Manager
PCT	Primary Care Trust
PGEA	Postgraduate Educational Allowance
PRINCE	PRojects IN Controlled Environment
QALY	Quality Adjusted Life Year
RCGP	Royal College of General Practitioners
RCN	Royal College of Nursing
RHA	Regional Health Authority
SHO	Senior House Officer
SI	Systeme International (units)
TQM	Total Quality Management
UKCC	United Kingdom Council for Nursing Midwifery and Health Visiting
WHO	World Health Organization

Useful addresses

Association of Community Health Councils
362 Euston Road
London NW1
Tel: 0171 388 4874

Association of Health Centre and Practice Administrators (AHCPA)
c/o Royal College of General Practitioners
14 Princes Gate
London SW7 1PU
Tel: 0171 581 3232

Association of Medical Secretaries, Practice Administrators and Receptionists (AMSPAR)
Tavistock House North
Tavistock Square
London WC1H 9LN
Tel: 0171 387 6005

British Medical Association (BMA)
BMA House
Tavistock Square
London WC1H 9JP
Tel: 0171 387 4499

Department of Social Security (DSS)
Eileen House
Elephant and Castle
London SE1 6BY
Tel: 0171 703 6380

General Medical Council (GMC)
44 Hallam Street
London W1N 6AE
Tel: 0171 580 7642

GP Computer Centre
75 York Road
London SE1 7NT
Tel: 0171 620 0901

Health and Safety Executive
Broad Lane
Sheffield SE3 7HQ
Tel: 0114 289 2000

Health Service Commissioner (Ombudsman) for England
Church House
Great Smith Street
London SW1P 3BW
Tel: 0171 276 2035 or 3000
(Investigates complaints about health authorities in England)

Health Services Commissioner for Scotland
2nd Floor
11 Melville Crescent
Edinburgh EH3 7LU
Tel: 0131 225 7465

Health Services Commissioner for Wales
4th Floor
Pearl Assurance House
Greyfriars Road
Cardiff CF1 3AG
Tel: 01222 394621

Hospital Consultants and Specialists Association
The Old Court House
London Road
Ascot
Berks SL5 7EN
Tel: 01344 25052

Institute of Health and Care Development
St Bartholomew's Court
18 Christmas Street
Bristol BS1 5BT
Tel: 0117 929 1029

Institute of Health Services Management (IHSM)
7–10 Chandos Street
London W1M 9DE
Tel: 0171 460 7654

King's Fund
11–13 Cavendish Square
London W1M 0AN
Tel: 0171 307 2400

Medical Defence Union
3 Devonshire Place
London W1N 2EA
Tel: 0171 4486 6181

Medical Protection Society
50 Hallam Street
London W1N 6DE
Tel: 0171 637 0541

National Association of Health Authorities and Trusts (NAHAT)
26 Chapter Street
London SW1P 4ND
Tel: 0171 233 7388

National Council for Vocational Qualifications
222 Euston Road
London NW1 2BZ
Tel: 0171 387 3611

Royal College of General Practitioners
14 Princes Gate
Hyde Park
London SW7 1PU
Tel: 0171 581 3232

Royal College of Obstetricians and Gynaecologists
27 Sussex Place
Regents Park
London NW1 4RG
Tel: 0171 262 5425

Royal College of Nursing (UK)
Henrietta Place
London W1M 0AB
Tel: 0171 580 2646

Royal College of Pathologists
2 Carlton House Terrace
London SW1Y 5AF
Tel: 0171 930 5861

Royal College of Physicians
11 St Andrew's Place
London NW1 4LE
Tel: 0171 935 1174

Royal College of Physicians, Edinburgh
9 Queen Street
Edinburgh EH2 1JQ
Tel: 0131 225 7324

Royal College of Physicians and Surgeons of Glasgow
232–242 St Vincent Street
Glasgow G2 5RJ
Tel: 0141 221 6072

Royal College of Psychiatrists
17 Belgrave Square
London SW1X 8PG
Tel: 0171 235 2351

Royal College of Surgeons
Nicolson Street
Edinburgh EH8 9DW
Tel: 0131 556 6206

Royal College of Surgeons of England
35–43 Lincoln's Inn Fields
London WC2A 3PN
Tel: 0171 405 3474

Royal Society of Medicine
1 Wimpole Street
London W1M 8AE
Tel: 0171 408 2119

RSA Examinations Board
Westwood Way
Coventry CV4 8HS
Tel: 01203 470033

Index

Note: page references in *italics* indicate illustrations. There may also be text on these pages.